1

How many times can you find the word OGRE hidden in the grid?

Which of these Triceratops skeletons is the odd one out?

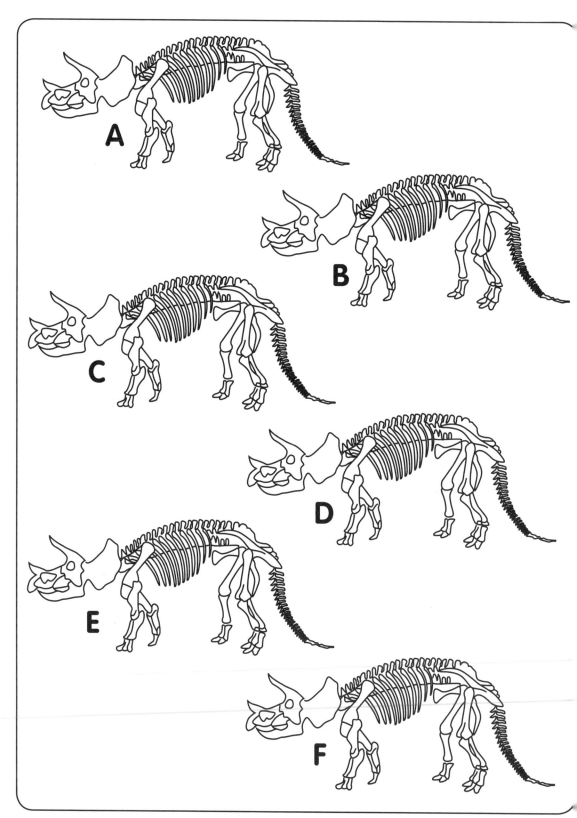

3 Add up the numbers on each pair of racing bikes to work out the sums.

249 + 561 =

436 + 700 =

128 + 642 =

732 + 119 =

4 Can you help the spider get through the web maze to end up in the centre?

5

Add your own colour to this supersonic scene.

This prehistoric watery world needs some colour adding.

Look back at the picture on page 6 for one minute. Now answer these questions without cheating!

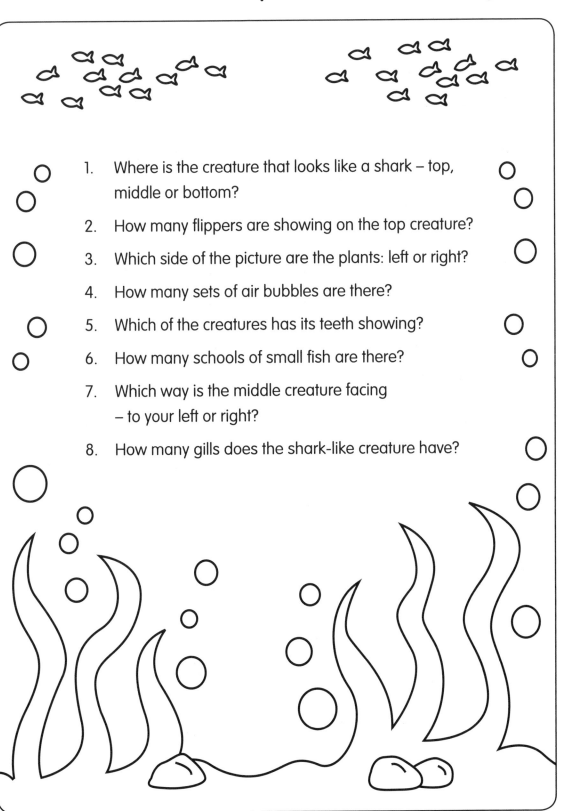

1. Where is the creature that looks like a shark – top, middle or bottom?

2. How many flippers are showing on the top creature?

3. Which side of the picture are the plants: left or right?

4. How many sets of air bubbles are there?

5. Which of the creatures has its teeth showing?

6. How many schools of small fish are there?

7. Which way is the middle creature facing – to your left or right?

8. How many gills does the shark-like creature have?

There are ten farm vehicles hidden in this grid – can you find them all?

```
C  O  M  B  Y  A  R  P  S  T  I  L
T  B  H  T  I  L  L  E  R  Q  U  A
B  I  A  A  R  O  T  C  A  R  T  Q
Q  A  L  S  R  A  R  O  O  H  T  U
A  U  X  H  E  R  A  I  A  G  R  A
R  Q  A  P  L  P  O  B  T  U  A  D
T  R  A  D  A  S  S  W  I  O  I  O
U  C  O  M  B  I  N  E  L  L  L  B
T  O  T  O  P  I  C  K  U  P  E  A
R  X  L  C  O  P  K  T  C  A  R  T
A  O  S  P  R  A  Y  E  R  Q  U  A
I  Q  W  C  O  M  B  P  L  O  U  G
```

COMBINE   TRACTOR   TRAILER

BALER   PICKUP

QUAD BIKE   PLOUGH   TILLER

HARROW   SPRAYER

Which of the jigsaw pieces completes the picture?

A

B

C

How many of the different bones can you count in this archaeological dig?

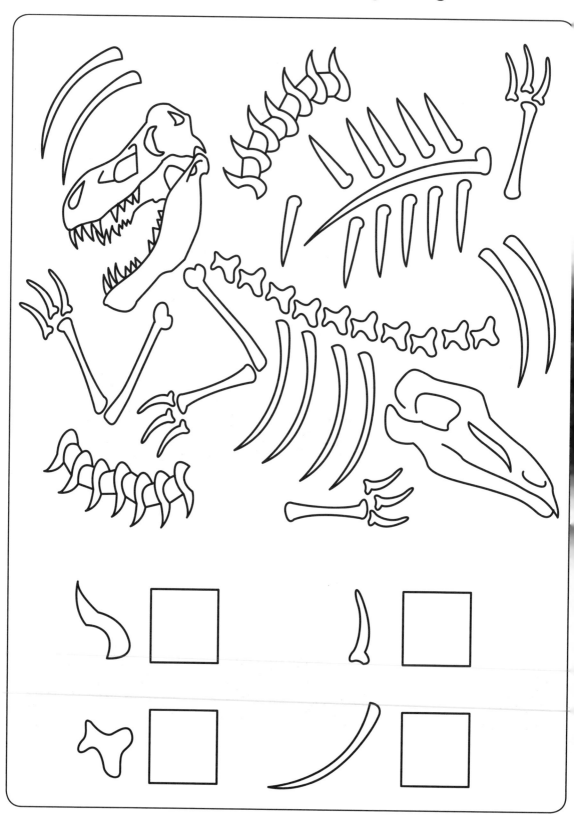

Colour in this beautiful sunny sailing scene.

Which of the naughty gnomes has hidden the fairy treasure? Use the clues to find out.

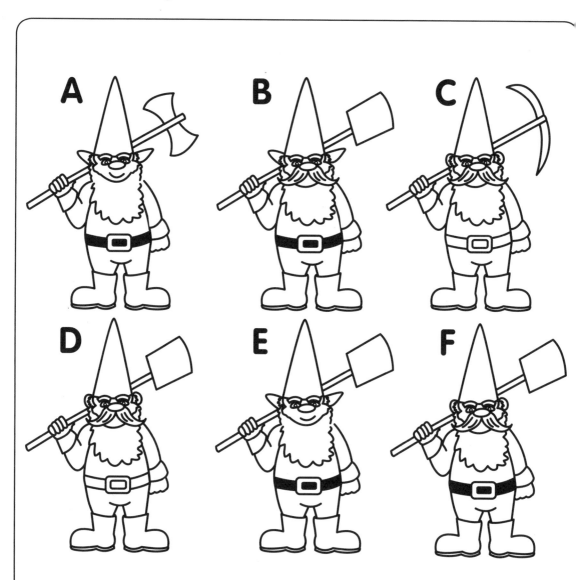

1. He is carrying a spade.

2. His belt is black.

3. His ears are pointy.

4. He has a moustache and a beard.

13

Help this early mammal escape from Struthiomimus.

START

FINISH

Solve the clues to fill in the missing letters. Each answer begins with S and ends with T.

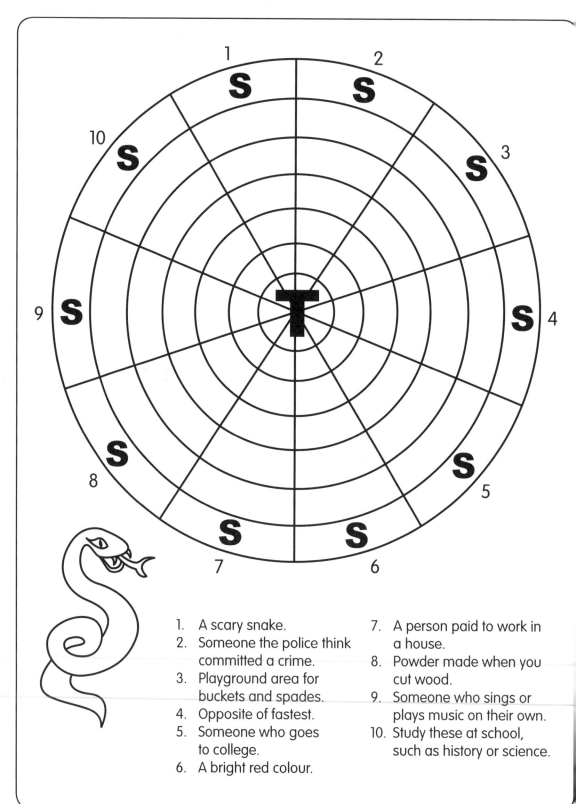

1. A scary snake.
2. Someone the police think committed a crime.
3. Playground area for buckets and spades.
4. Opposite of fastest.
5. Someone who goes to college.
6. A bright red colour.
7. A person paid to work in a house.
8. Powder made when you cut wood.
9. Someone who sings or plays music on their own.
10. Study these at school, such as history or science.

Parasaurolophus may have been very noisy and colourful!

Read the clues carefully and put ticks in the correct boxes to work out who has each present, and what colour it is.

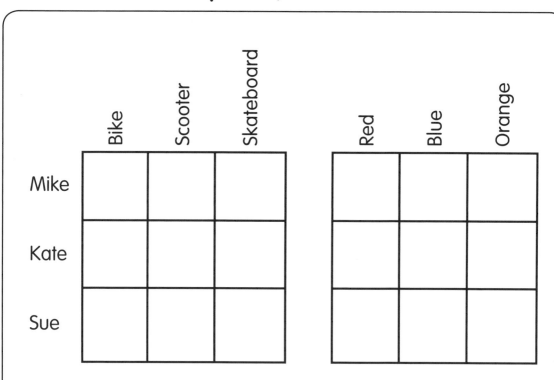

	Bike	Scooter	Skateboard		Red	Blue	Orange
Mike							
Kate							
Sue							

1. One girl has a scooter but it isn't red.

2. Kate's present is red and has pedals.

3. Sue's present isn't blue and you don't sit on it.

4. The orange present isn't Mike's.

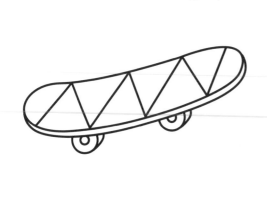

Hurray! Colour the van and the yummy ice creams.

18 Help the zombie find his way back to his grave by finding the correct path using numbers from the six times table.

10   16   32   18   40   11   1

6   12   24   60   12   20

14   44   50   16   48   15   8

7   64   35   28   18   11   16

2   6   54   60   36   30   14

3   20   52   12   28   19   46   52

22   9   60   42   24   30   18   5

17   21   19   13   44

51   4

RIP

19 There are ten differences between these two pictures. Can you spot them all?

20   Fill in the missing numbers on the train
to count through the 7 times table.

21

These Kentrosaurus need some bright colours and patterns.

Can you do the monster match? One of these monsters has a reflection. Find them both!

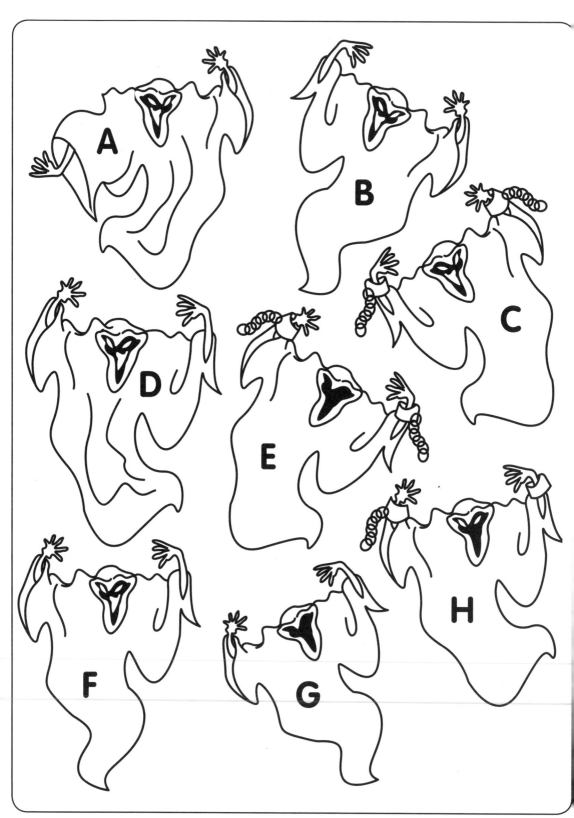

How many times can you find the word SAIL hidden in the grid?

```
          S
        S A I
      S A L S A
      A L S A I L
    A S L S A L S L
    S A I A L S A I S
    S S A I L A I S S A
  S A A L S L I L S A I A
  A I L S L A I S A I L L S
  I L S A I I A L S L I S A
```

24   Solve the sudoku puzzle so that every row, column and mini-grid has each of the six symbols.

Fill in this high-speed train with eye-catching colours.

26 Can you find the ten fancy dress costumes hidden in the grid? They can appear up and down, diagonally, and backwards or forwards.

```
i  e  r  i  p  m  a  v  f  s
c  a  r  y  g  m  u  m  m  y
d  b  a  n  s  h  e  e  b  e
r  i  n  o  c  g  o  s  c  n
a  a  n  t  b  e  s  s  i  e
z  e  i  e  e  n  c  l  t  i
i  w  h  l  a  n  b  c  e  b
w  e  r  e  w  o  l  f  s  m
a  r  e  k  g  i  t  s  h  o
a  l  l  s  o  w  e  e  n  z
```

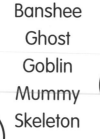

Banshee
Ghost
Goblin
Mummy
Skeleton

Vampire
Werewolf
Witch
Wizard
Zombie

When you have found them all, the remaining letters spell out a message.

Choose from the body bits here to draw your own custom-made monsters!

The mini-grid appears only once in the whole of the larger grid. Can you find it?

This Archaeopteryx can have any colour feathers you like.

Work out which letters of the alphabet are missing from this muddle. Use them to spell the name of a tradesman

What colour will this cement mixer be when you have finished work?

Follow the instructions to find three armoured dinosaurs hidden on the dino-clock.

Write down the two letters shown by the minute hand, then the two letters shown by the hour hand.
Do this for every time and you will spell out a dinosaur's name. For example, half past eleven = PIKE.

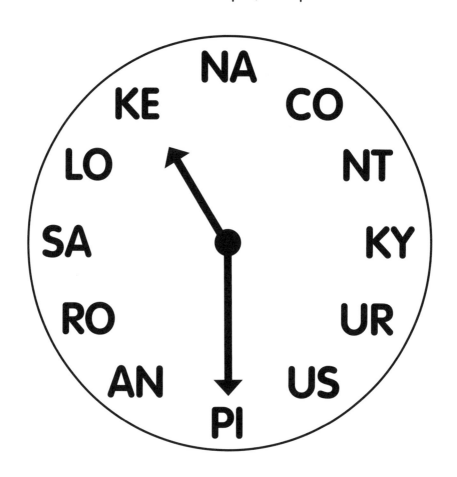

1. Twenty five to three, ten to nine, twenty past five =

2. Five to two, twenty to nine, twenty past five =

3. Half past twelve, five past nine, twenty past five =

See if you can solve these maths problems without a calculator.

1. If a motorbike travels at 100 kilometres an hour, how far will it travel in 1.5 hours?

2. A car uses 7 litres of fuel to travel 100 kilometres. How much fuel does it use to travel 400 kilometres?

3. A train has travelled 500 kilometres in 2.5 hours. How fast was it going?

4. In one day, a car showroom sells 8 less Ferraris than Porsches. Altogether, they sell 12 cars. How many Porsches do they sell?

5. A train has 14 carriages. All of them are red or white, and there are 4 more red carriages than white ones. How many red carriages are there?

Can you turn WOLF into MOON by changing one letter at a time? Each change must use a real word. Use the clues to help you.

WOLF

_ _ _ _ The noise of a dog

_ _ _ _ Material from trees

_ _ _ _ How you are feeling

MOON

**Here's a spooky game you can play at parties.
You need at least five players.**

Draw a cross on a scrap of paper and scrunch it up. Scrunch up more pieces (one for each player) and put them in a bowl Each player picks out a piece; the one who gets the cross is the 'Murderer' and must keep it secret.

Sit in a large circle. The players look at each other in any order they like. The idea is that the Murderer must wink at someone, without the others noticing.
The winked-at person has been 'murdered', and can make a big, noisy deal of dying.

Anyone who thinks they know who the Murderer is can accuse them, but if they get it wrong they're out of the game.

Try to figure out who is the Murderer before all of the players become victims to his or her winking ways!

Which of the silhouettes is an exact match for the picture of the dune buggy?

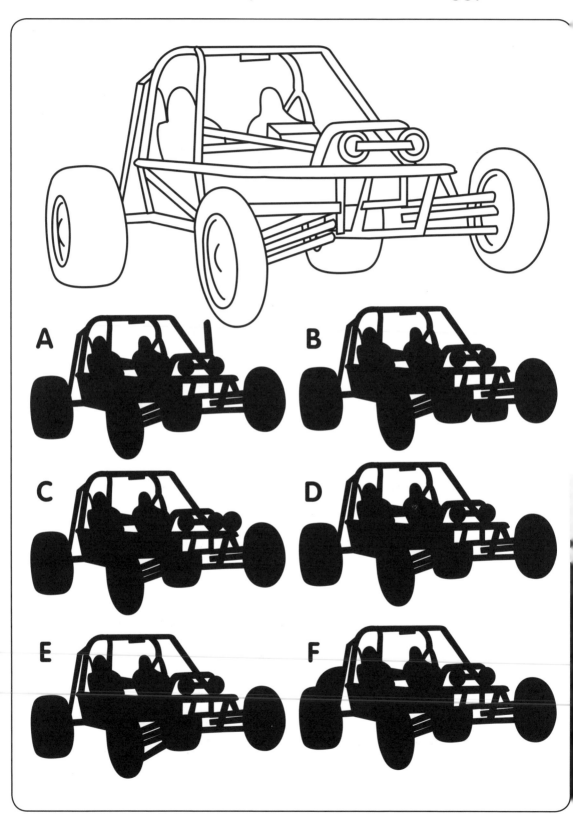

Can you help the Brachiosaurus through the dusty land to reach water?

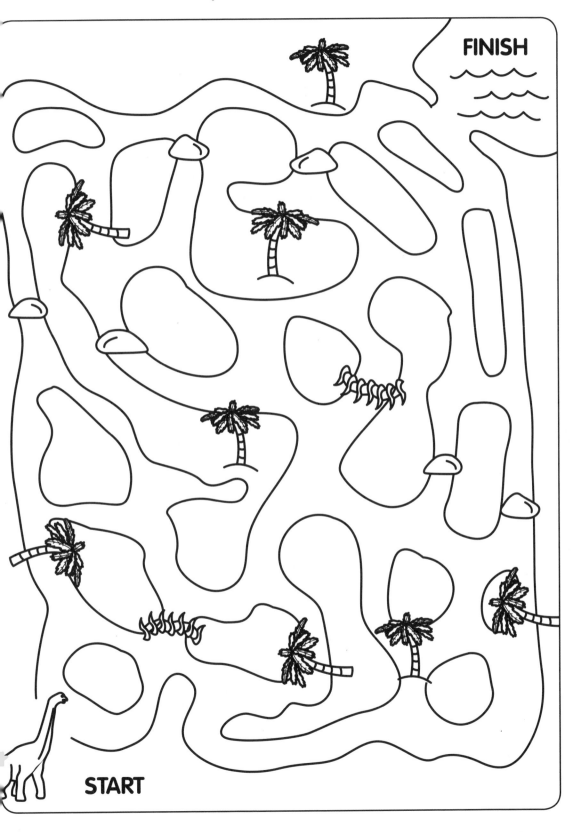

FINISH

START

Add up the 3-figure numbers on the skull dice to work out the sums.

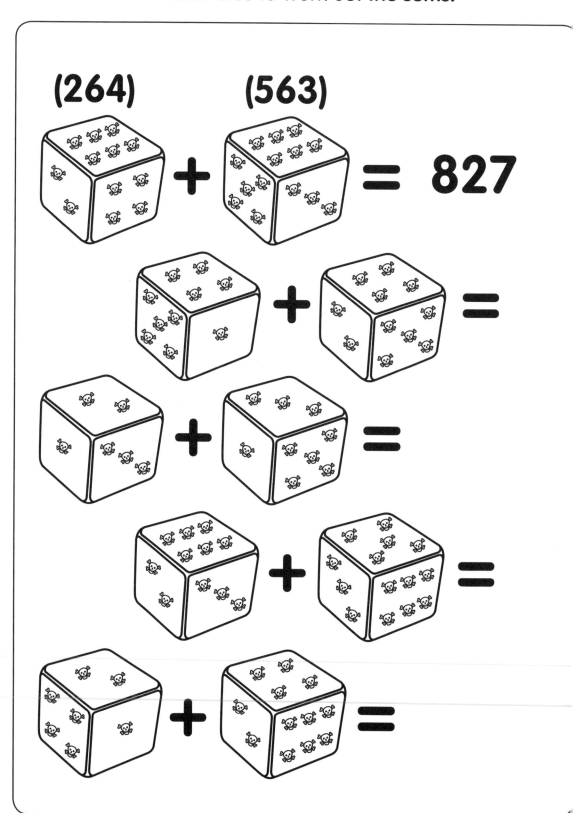

(264) **(563)**

+ **= 827**

+ **=**

+ **=**

+ **=**

+ **=**

Colour in this huge Alamosaurus, America's biggest dinosaur.

40 Cross out any double letters in each section, and use the remaining letters to spell three spooky words.

41 Match each number held by the monster to another number to make pairs that add up to 1000.

Use space-age colours to make this
scene truly out-of-this-world!

Follow the footprints to work out which weapon belongs to each ghostly knight.

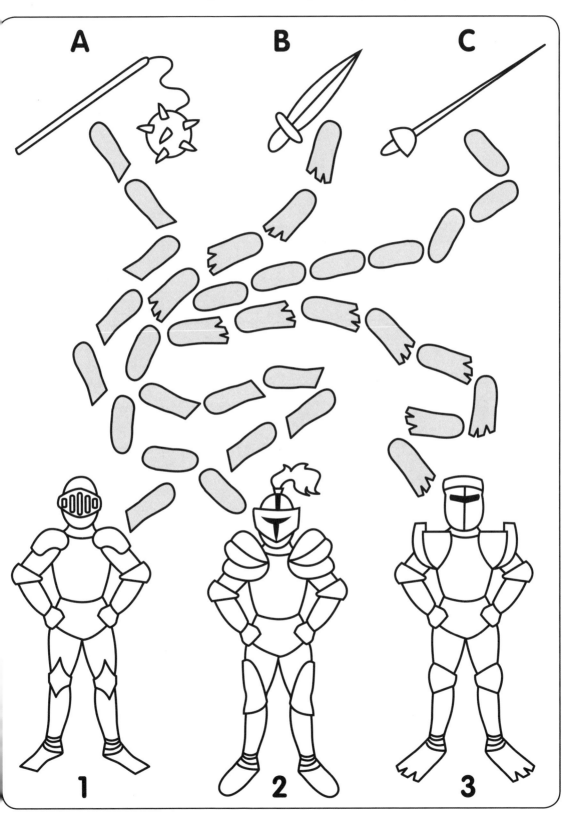

Answer the joke by colouring all the squares with the letters D, N or L and seeing what letters are left.

Why did the
dinosaur bounce?

D	I	D	L	N	D	T	L	N	L
L	L	D	N	D	L	N	N	N	D
W	D	N	L	A	L	S	L	D	D
N	L	N	L	D	L	D	N	N	L
L	A	D	L	D	N	D	L	L	N
L	D	L	D	D	L	N	L	L	N
L	D	T	N	R	D	L	N	N	I
D	C	L	D	L	E	N	R	N	A
L	L	D	N	D	L	D	L	L	N
D	H	L	O	P	N	S	L	L	N

Follow the clues to find out
who wins the race.

The car with the star on it comes last.

The grey car comes behind the ones
with black stripes and a black bonnet.

The checked car is ahead of three others.

The car with black stripes is just in front of the car with checks.

Fill in the numbers following the instructions. The answer in the top dino egg is how many million years ago Argentinosaurus was around.

The number in each egg is the total of the two numbers below it.

For example, the shaded number is 3 because 1 + 2 = 3.

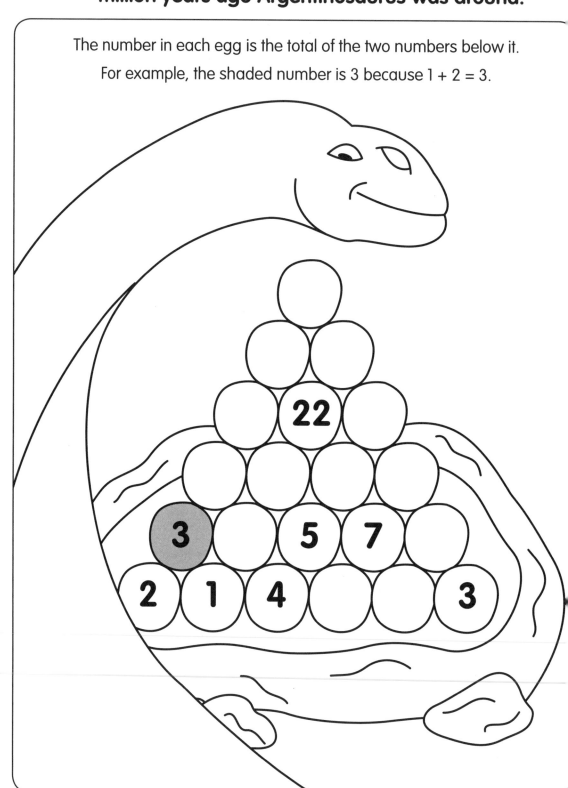

Solve the riddle, line by line, to find which vehicle is being spelt out.

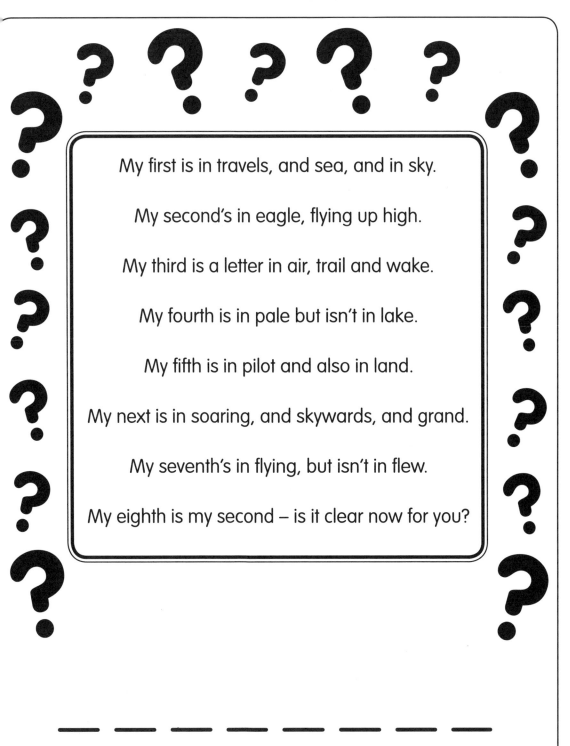

My first is in travels, and sea, and in sky.

My second's in eagle, flying up high.

My third is a letter in air, trail and wake.

My fourth is in pale but isn't in lake.

My fifth is in pilot and also in land.

My next is in soaring, and skywards, and grand.

My seventh's in flying, but isn't in flew.

My eighth is my second – is it clear now for you?

_ _ _ _ _ _ _ _

Colour the patterns on this baby Parasaurolophus.

Can you find the word PIXIE hidden only once in the grid? It can read across or down, backwards or diagonally.

```
      I   X   I
      X   I   E
      I   I   X
  P   E   P   P
  I   I   I   I   E   P
X   X   X   X   X   X   I
P   I   I   E   E   X   X   P
X   P   P   I   E   I   I   I
P   I   X   E   P   I   X   X
E   X   I   P   X   I   P   I
```

Which of the silhouettes matches the Pterosaur?

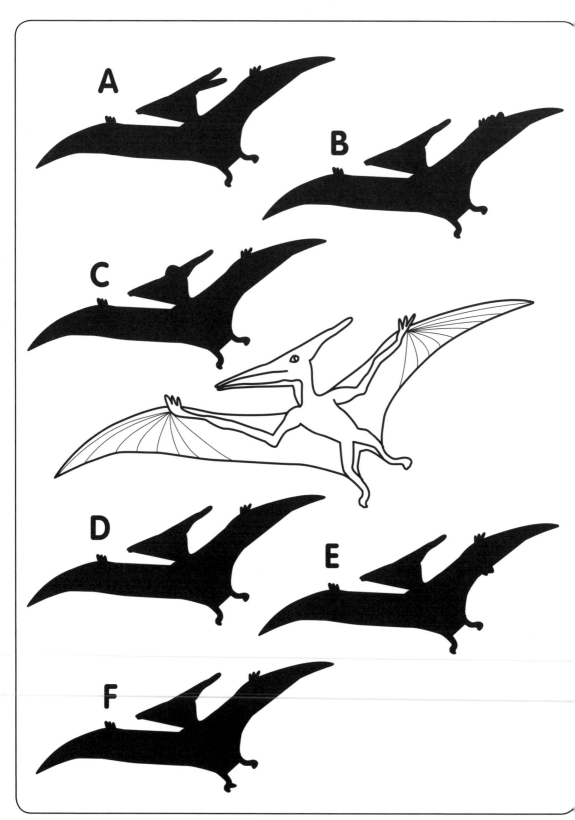

You'll have to be quick with your colours
to keep up with these drivers!

How many bones can you count on this page? And how many skulls are there?

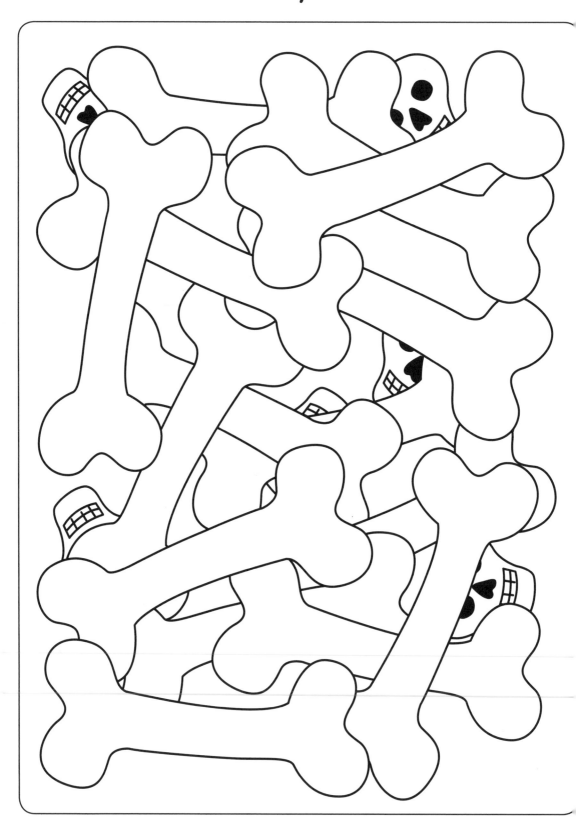

53 Study the sequence of pictures carefully and work out which of the wizards finishes the pattern: a, b or c?

A   B   C

If A=1, B=2, C=3 and so on, work out what type
of car these licence plates are for.

6.5.18.18.1.18.9

3.9.20.18.15.5.14

13.3.12.1.18.5.14

18.5.14.1.21.12.20

8.25.21.14.4.1.9

Add some colour to this archaeological find.

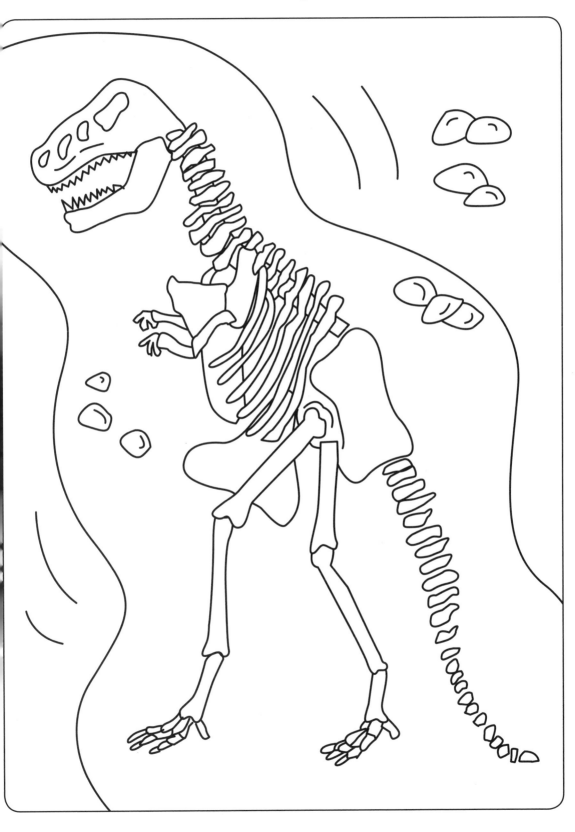

Don't miss your flight! Match each flight time to the correct clock.

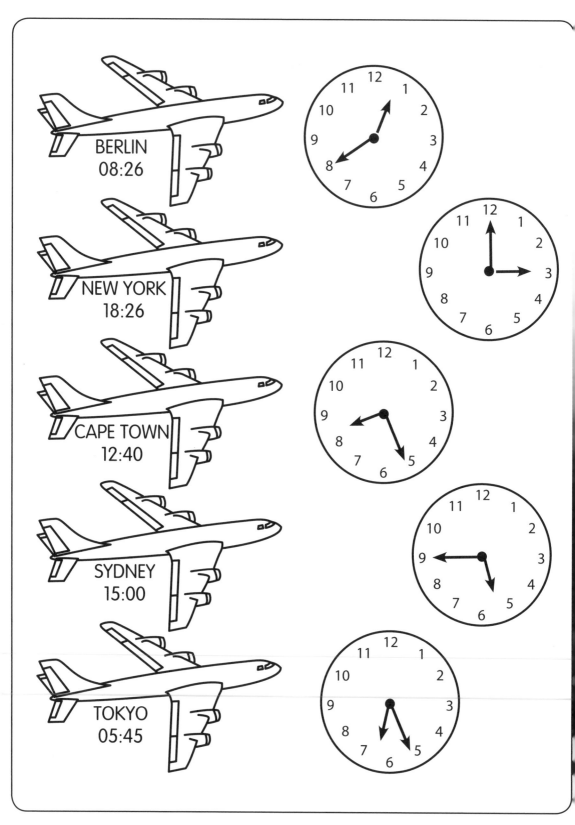

BERLIN
08:26

NEW YORK
18:26

CAPE TOWN
12:40

SYDNEY
15:00

TOKYO
05:45

57 How many smaller words can you make from the letters below? Two are listed to get you started.

BEWARE THE JABBERWOCK

WEATHER

BEAR

Answer the questions to fill in the code and open the spooky safe!

1. How many spiders can you see?
2. What number is the clock hand pointing to?
3. How many candlesticks are there?
4. How many logs are in the fireplace?

Have fun finishing this picture with bright colours.

60   Fill in the puzzle so that every row, column and
mini-grid has each of the four footprints.

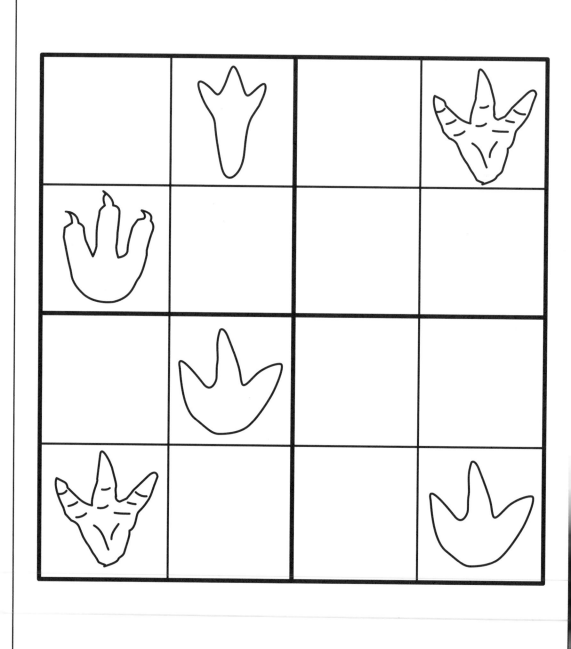

Use the vehicles with less than four wheels to spell the name of a city that is famous for its motor race.

62 These creatures lived in the water in prehistoric times. Colour them in ocean shades.

Match each of Cerberus's three heads to the correct equation underneath.

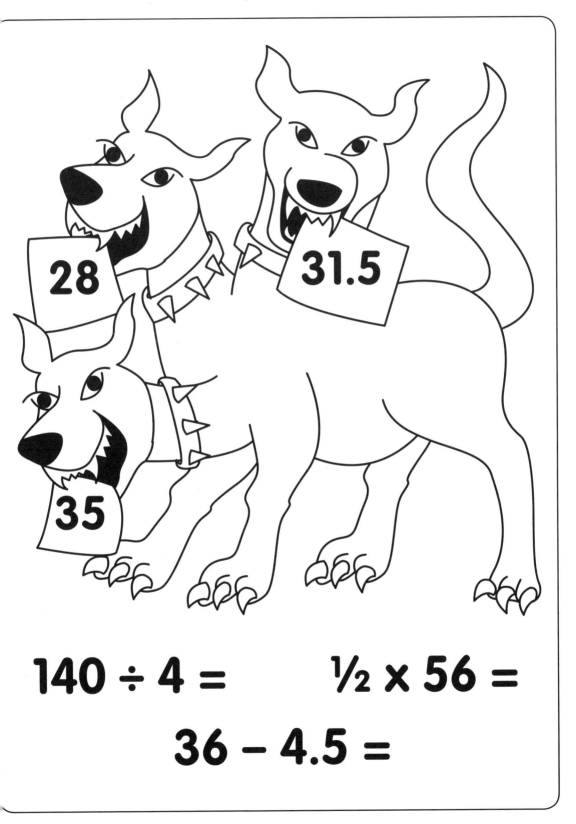

$140 \div 4 =$ $\frac{1}{2} \times 56 =$

$36 - 4.5 =$

64   Can you find your way out of the building to escape from King Kong at the top?

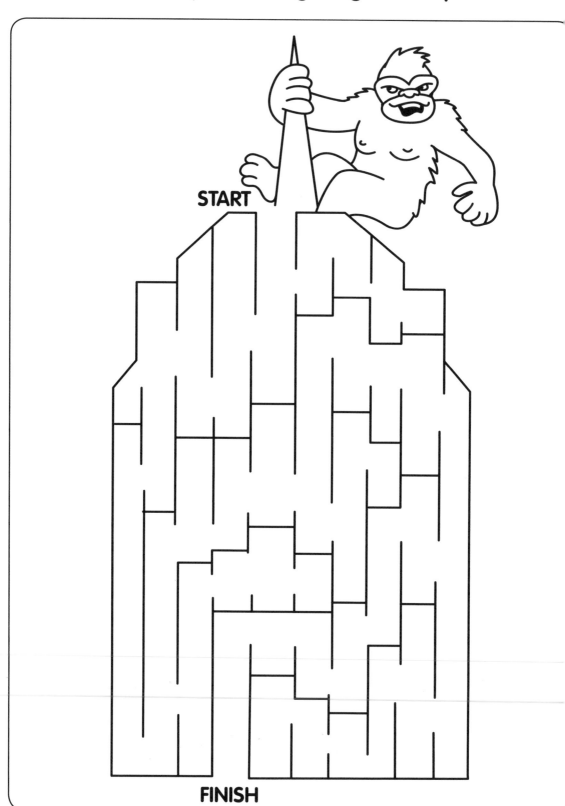

START

FINISH

Cross out every other letter, starting with D, to find what has made these footprints.

~~D~~ C T A Y R A N K

O U T A P T S O

R E U X S

Whisk yourself away to a watery world as you colour.

Count through the four times table to guide the Stegosaurus through the forest.

Start at the letter P and trace your way through the grid to find 15 words related to trains.

```
P  A  S  S  E  C  K  S  T  A
C  I  T  R  N  A  I  E  R  T
K  E  T  E  G  R  G  H  F  I
I  R  C  R  D  T  D  T  N  O
A  R  A  A  R  I  I  E  S  E
G  V  E  U  T  C  G  I  N  L
E  I  R  G  C  E  N  C  E  S
L  R  D  E  E  L  E  A  O  T
O  M  O  V  W  A  Y  R  G  E
C  O  T  I  L  I  A  R  M  A
```

What's going on in the darkness? Reveal all with your torch, and then draw it…

70   Read the clues carefully and put ticks in the boxes to work out who is going where, and how much their fare is.

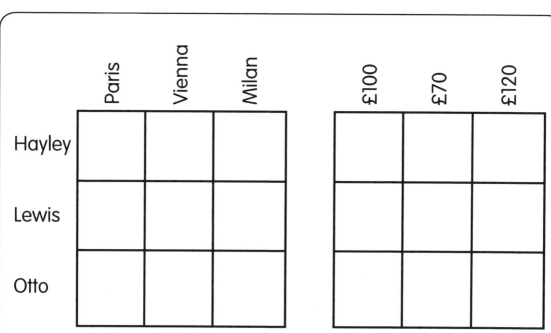

	Paris	Vienna	Milan		£100	£70	£120
Hayley							
Lewis							
Otto							

1. Lewis is paying more than Otto but less than Hayley.

2. Hayley isn't going to Paris.

3. Otto isn't going to a capital city.

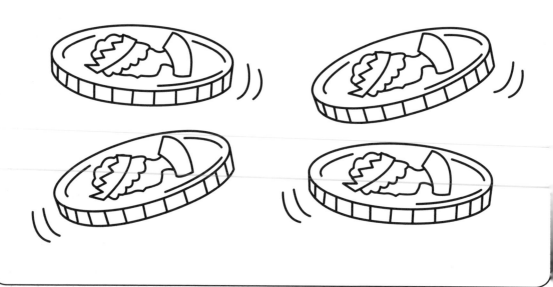

Use the dinosaur eggs containing prime numbers to spell the name of a fast, lightweight predator.

_ _ _ _ _ _ _

The mini-grid appears only once in the whole of the larger grid. Can you find it?

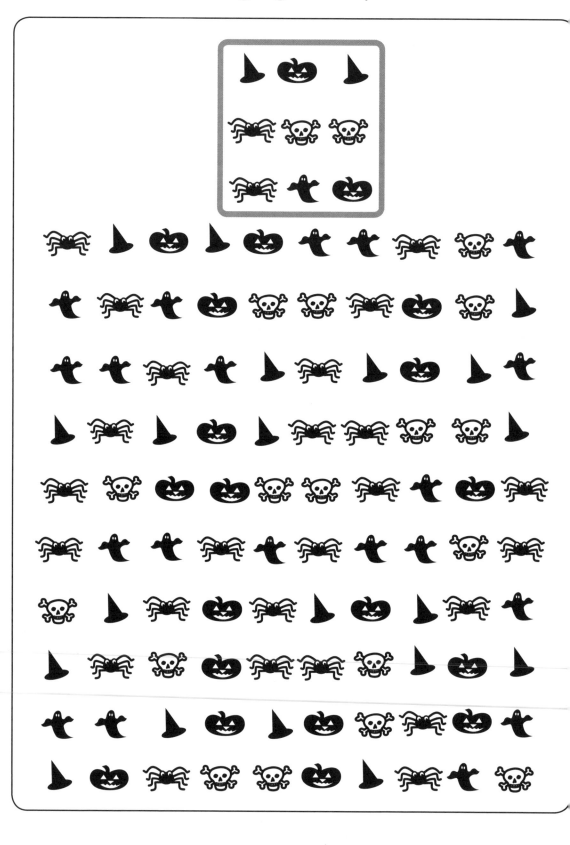

This horned dinosaur can be any colour you choose.

This party game is known as Witchy Woo, or Blind Man's Buff. It's fun to play with lots of people in a large room or hall.

One person plays the Witch, and must be gently blindfolded. She should not be able to see anything (but don't hurt her by tying it too tightly). Close any doors so she doesn't accidentally roam outside!

The Witch must move around the room with her arms stretched in front of her, and try to touch another player. The first person to be touched will be the next Witch. The last player to be touched is the winner.

If you are the Witch, use your other senses to help you find a victim. Listen for giggles and shouts, or feel the air move as someone charges past you.

If you are playing in a smaller room, add the rule that no one must move their feet. You can duck down or bob sideways to avoid a touch, but have to stay in one place.

Find out what Apatosaurus used to be called by decoding the message. The sides of the grid square tell you where to look,
eg A = _| while G = |_ and S = ¬

A	D	G
B•	E•	H•
••C	••F	••I

J	M	P
K•	N•	Q•
••L	••O	••R

S	V	Y
T•	W•	Z•
••U	••X	

_B R O N T O S A U R U S_

_ _ _ _ _ _ _ _ _ _ _ _

How many smaller words can you make from the letters below? Two are listed to get you started.

CHEQUERED FLAG

EQUAL

GLAD

What colours do you need for this amazing sky-high view?

Which of the bones should the hound choose?
He only wants ones with numbers from the
nine times table.

Look carefully to find two new passengers on this bus.

80 Find a way through the school corridors as quickly as you can to escape from the Demon Headmaster!

FINISH

81 Add the first number to the second, the second to the third, and so on, to fill the gaps on the ladder.

Which of the silhouettes exactly matches the main picture?

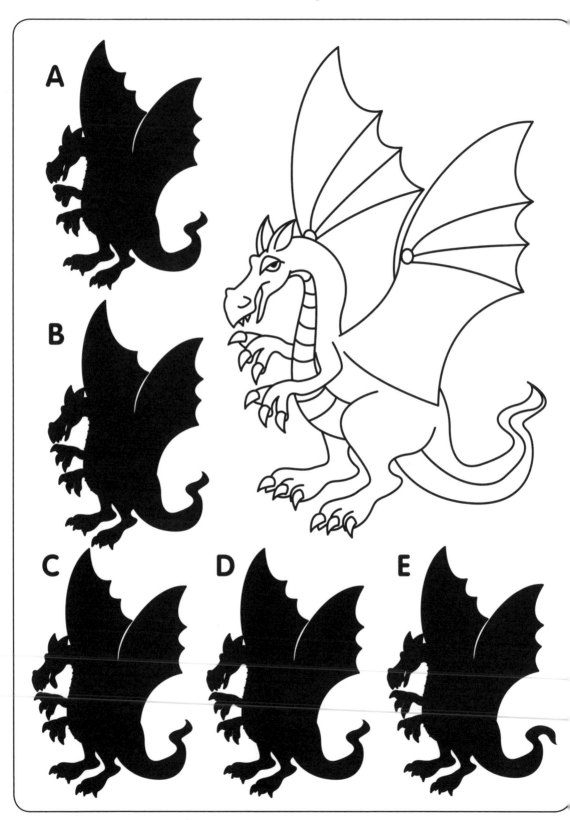

Where is this Heterodontosaurus headed?
Colour it as it runs.

Which of these hands is holding a sum that equals 13?

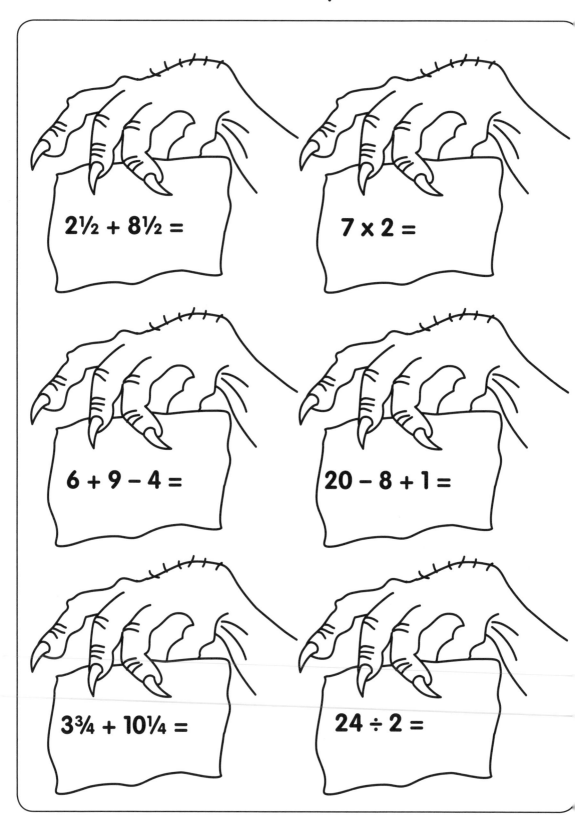

$2\frac{1}{2} + 8\frac{1}{2} =$

$7 \times 2 =$

$6 + 9 - 4 =$

$20 - 8 + 1 =$

$3\frac{3}{4} + 10\frac{1}{4} =$

$24 \div 2 =$

**Cross out all of the letters O, T and R to
find the name for the bullet train in Japan.**

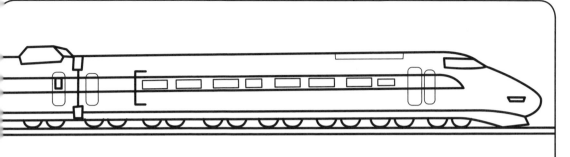

T R O R O R T T R O
O S R O H O O R T O
R O O T I N T O O T
T O K T O R T A R O
R O T T R O T O O T
T O R O N T O R T O
S T R O O E R O N O
R O O T O O T O O T

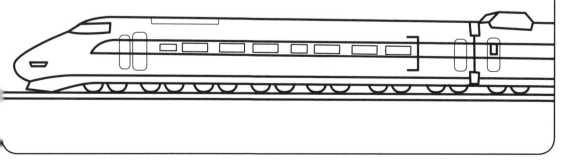

Solve the sudoku puzzle so that every row, column and mini-grid has each of the six symbols.

Each pair of words has a missing word in the middle
that acts as a link to both. One has been done
to show you how it works.

SPIDER _ _ _ SITE

FUNNY _ _ _ _ DRY

BAD <u>BLOOD</u> BROTHER

BLACK _ _ _ _ _ _ SPELL

CANDLE _ _ _ _ _ _ INSECT

DRAGON _ _ _ FISHING

FULL _ _ _ _ BEAM

Which of these Gallimimus is not exactly the same as the others?

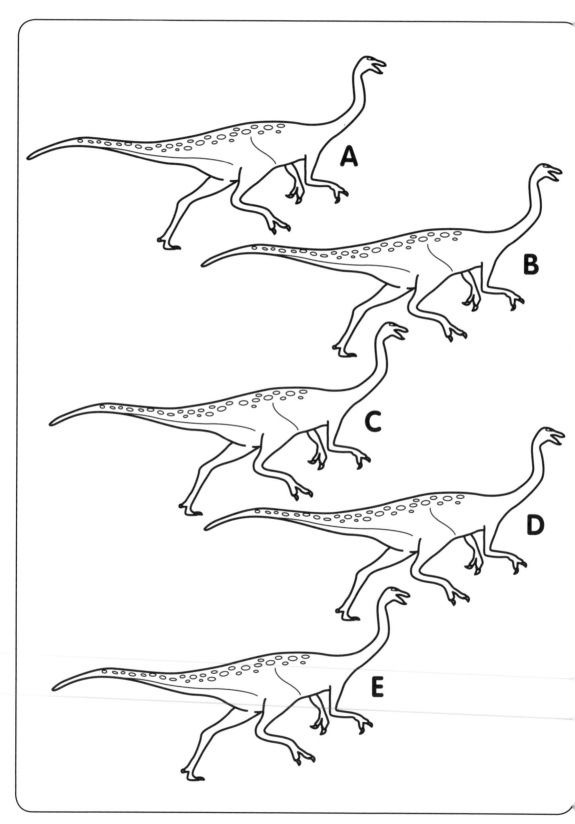

Add some colour to this busy scene.

Fill in the missing digits to make the magic spell formulas work properly.

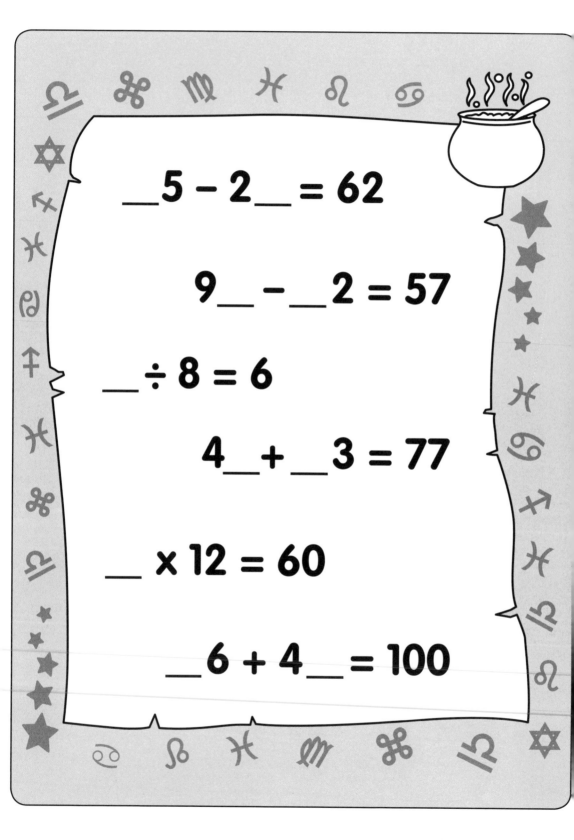

__5 − 2__ = 62

9__ − __2 = 57

__ ÷ 8 = 6

4__ + __3 = 77

__ × 12 = 60

__6 + 4__ = 100

What kind of creature has appeared in this moonlit clearing? You decide!

Do the sums to work out which driver belongs to each car.

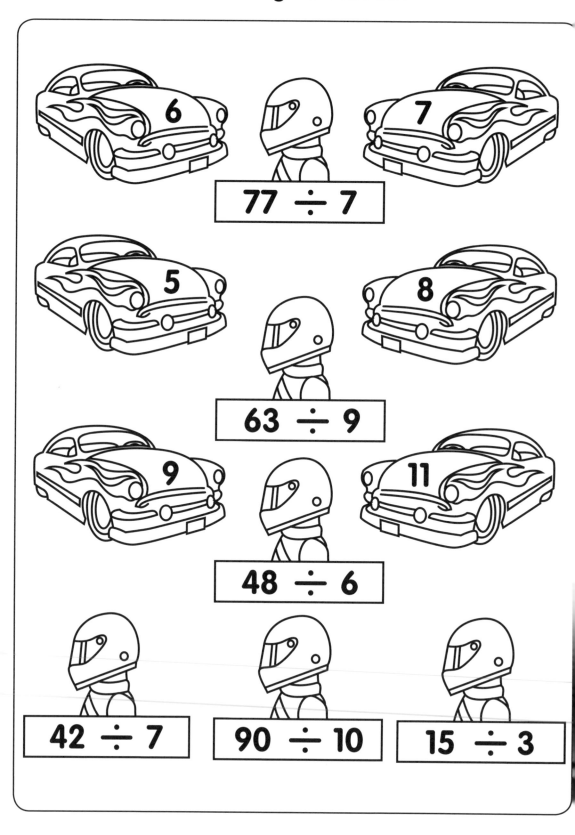

6

7

77 ÷ 7

5

8

63 ÷ 9

9

11

48 ÷ 6

42 ÷ 7

90 ÷ 10

15 ÷ 3

Which group of letters cannot be unscrambled to spell STEGOSAURUS correctly?

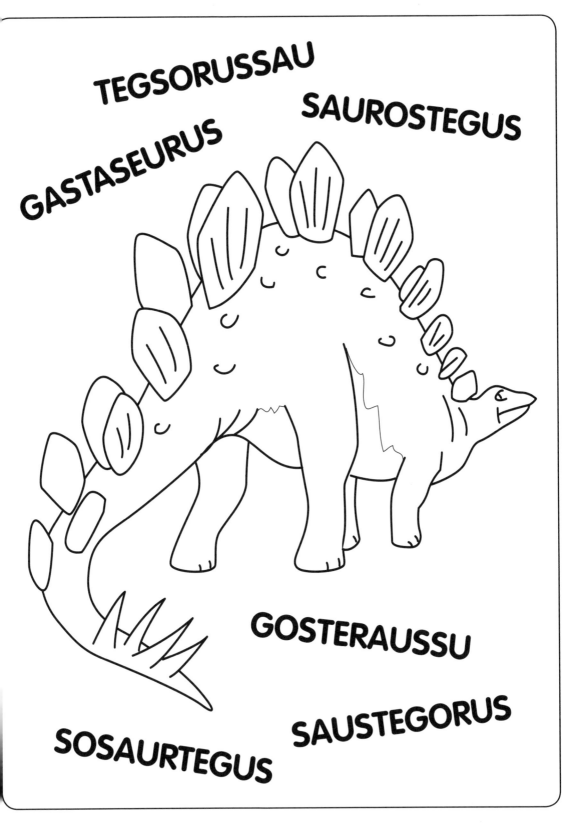

TEGSORUSSAU

SAUROSTEGUS

GASTASEURUS

GOSTERAUSSU

SAUSTEGORUS

SOSAURTEGUS

Help the tractor to find a way out of the fields.

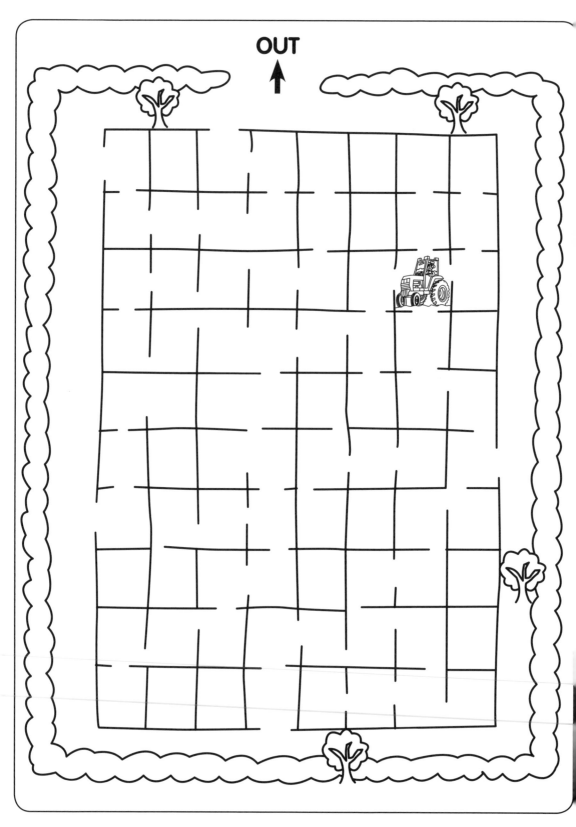

Plateosaurus was an early plant-eater.
Can you colour it?

Can you rearrange the six pictures so they tell the werewolf story in the correct order?

Velociraptor was one of the cleverest dinosaurs, but can you help it get through the grid using numbers from the 7 times table?

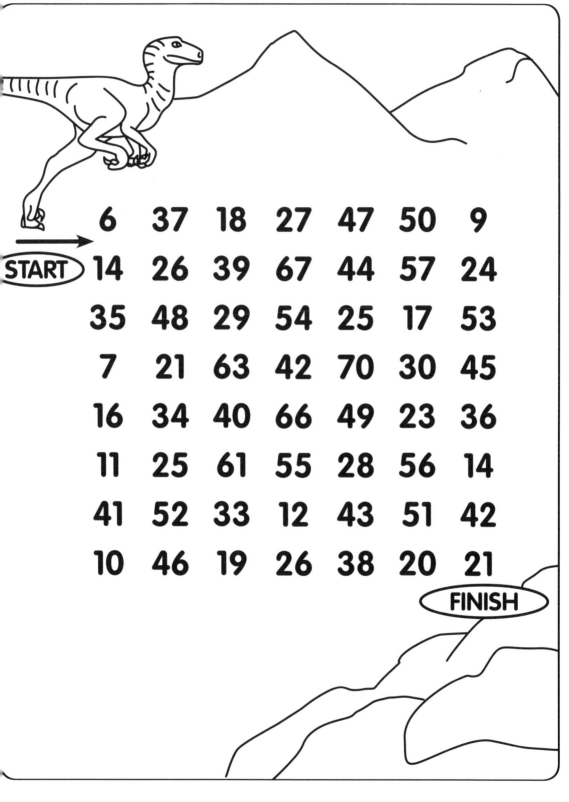

6	37	18	27	47	50	9
14	26	39	67	44	57	24
35	48	29	54	25	17	53
7	21	63	42	70	30	45
16	34	40	66	49	23	36
11	25	61	55	28	56	14
41	52	33	12	43	51	42
10	46	19	26	38	20	21

START

FINISH

Which of the jigsaw pieces
fills the gap?

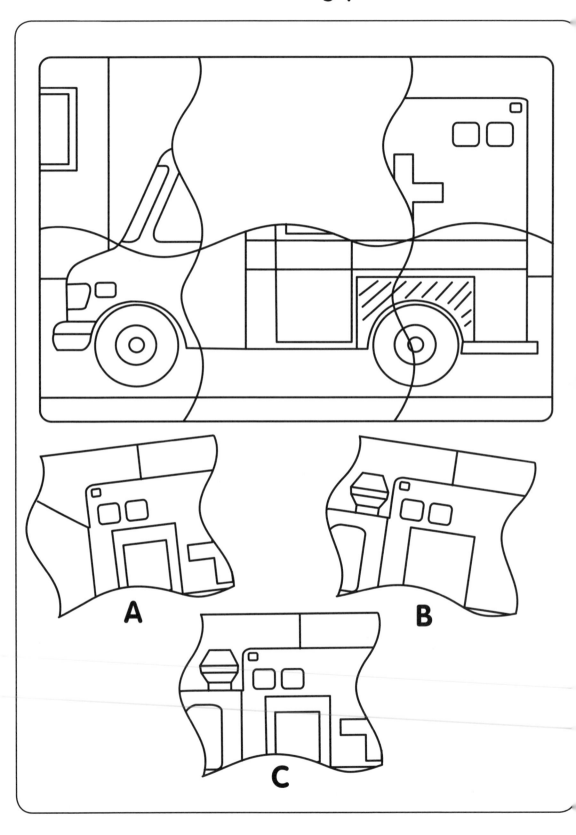

A

B

C

Make this a winter wonderland with a colourful snow mobile.

100 Fit the words into the grid and the circled letters will spell a kind of carriage pulled by a horse.

JEEP   CART

TANK

BOAT

Can you spot five differences between these two aliens?

Quickly, colour this raptor before it runs away!

Which of the abominable snowmen has stomped the farthest? Add up the numbers in each set of footprints to find out.

Which two T-rex are exactly the same?

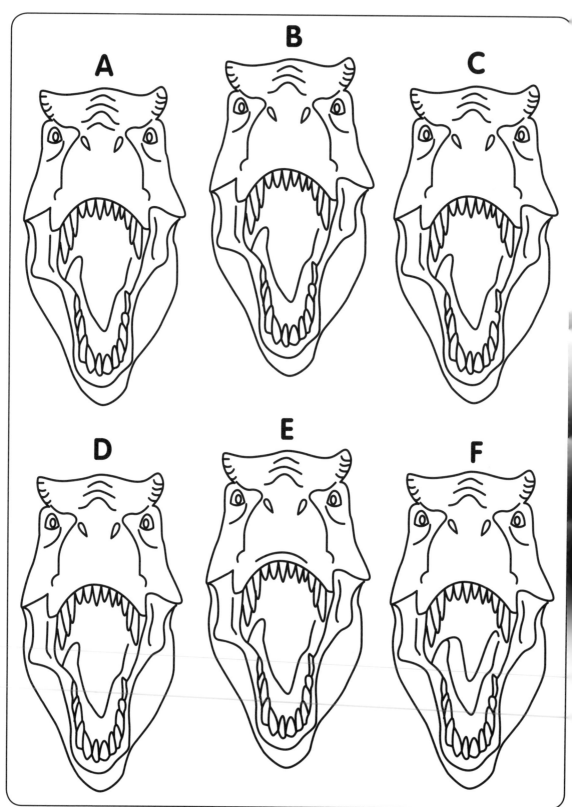

A

B

C

D

E

F

How many times can you find the word CLAW hidden in the grid?

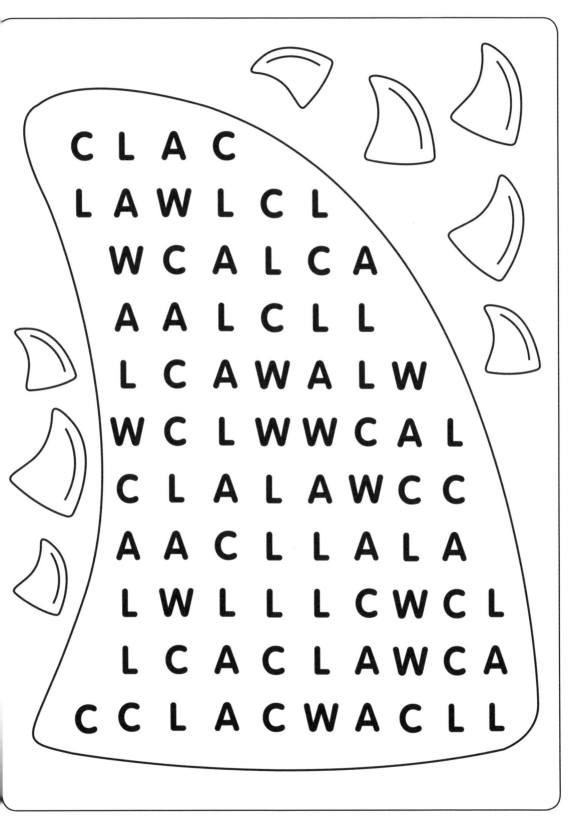

```
C L A C
L A W L C L
W C A L C A
A A L C L L
L C A W A L W
W C L W W C A L
C L A L A W C C
A A C L L A L A
L W L L L C W C L
L C A C L A W C A
C C L A C W A C L L
```

Add some eye-catching colours to this stunt bike.

Cross out any letter that appears twice and rearrange those left to spell which working vehicle the keys belong to.

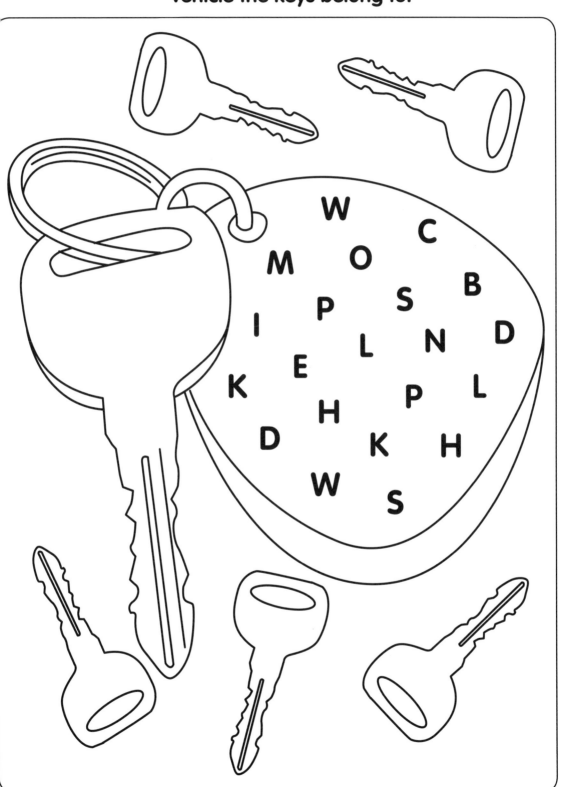

108 Fill in the puzzle so that every row, column and mini-grid has each of the four wheel pictures.

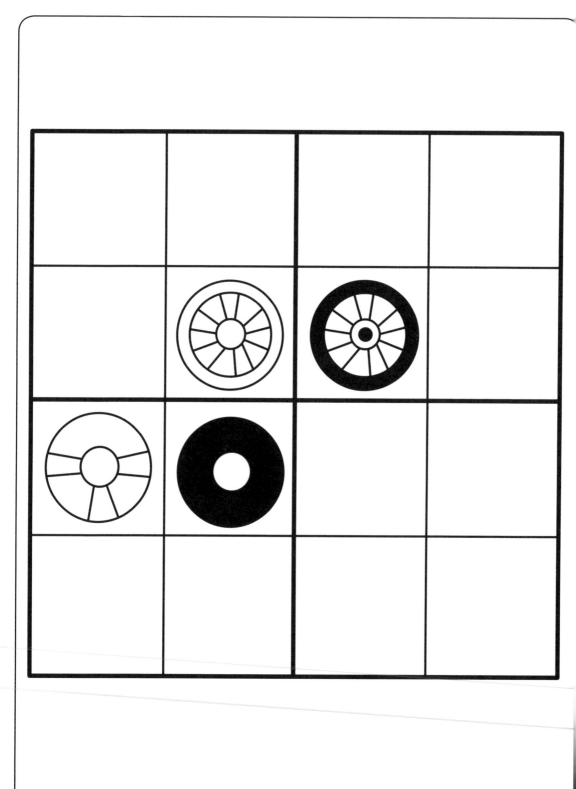

Study the main picture of a Hallowe'en party, and then work out which of the smaller pictures is how the party would look from above.

110   **Follow the dino trail through the grid, stepping from an egg to a claw to a footprint each time.**

Use the missing letters of the alphabet to spell a vehicle that can be fun as well as useful.

_ _ _ _ _ _ _ _ _

What colour will you make this pondersome plant-eater?

13

Which of these bells is Quasimodo actually ringing?

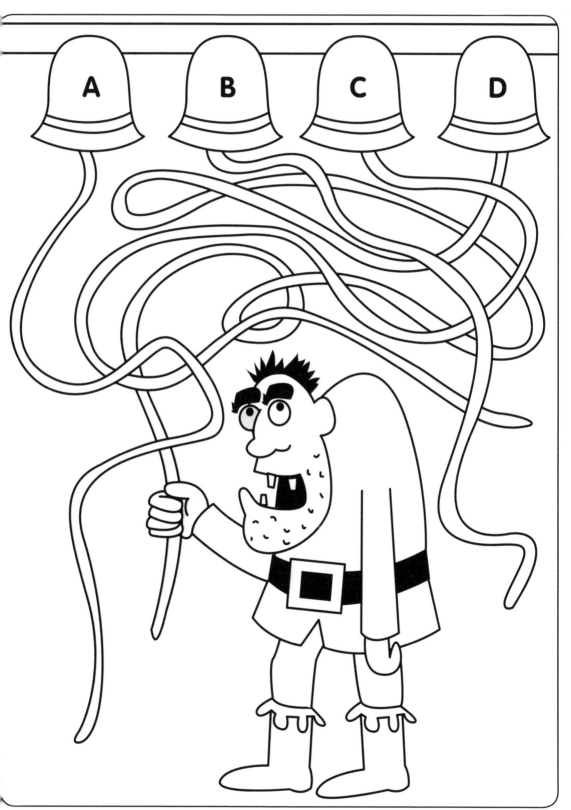

Can you find the word TRUCK hidden just once in the grid?

```
T T R U K C T R U
R R U C T T R R R
T U C K R U C T U
R U C T R U K R C
U C T K T T R U C
U K R T R R C C T
C R U R U U K K R
K T R U C U C K U
T R R K T R U C C
R U U T R U K C T
U K C K U T C T R
C C K U T R C K U
C U R T R U K K T
```

Which of these gargoyles is the odd one out?

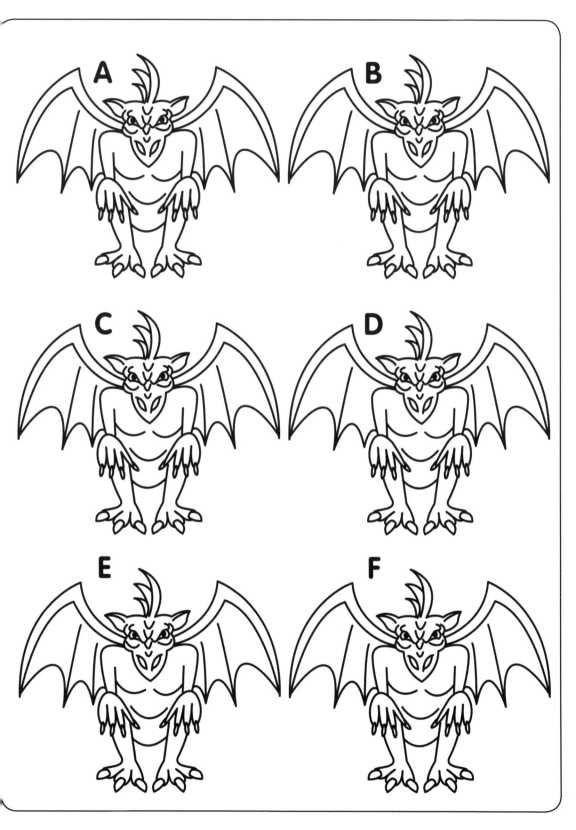

**Use sunny colours for this cruise ship
and its island stopover.**

117   **Fill in the missing numbers in the ogre's footprints to count through the 4 times table.**

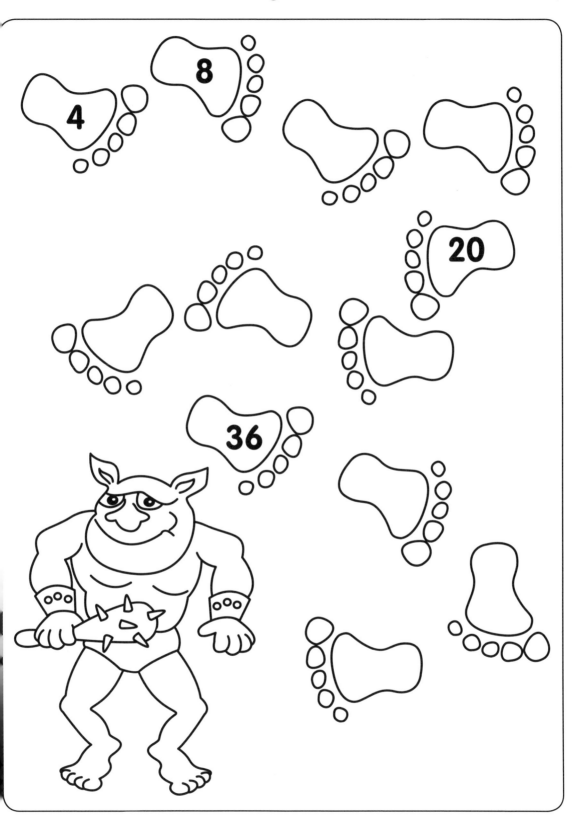

118 Use the clue letters to help you fit the car names in the grid. If you get them right, the circled letters will spell another car name.

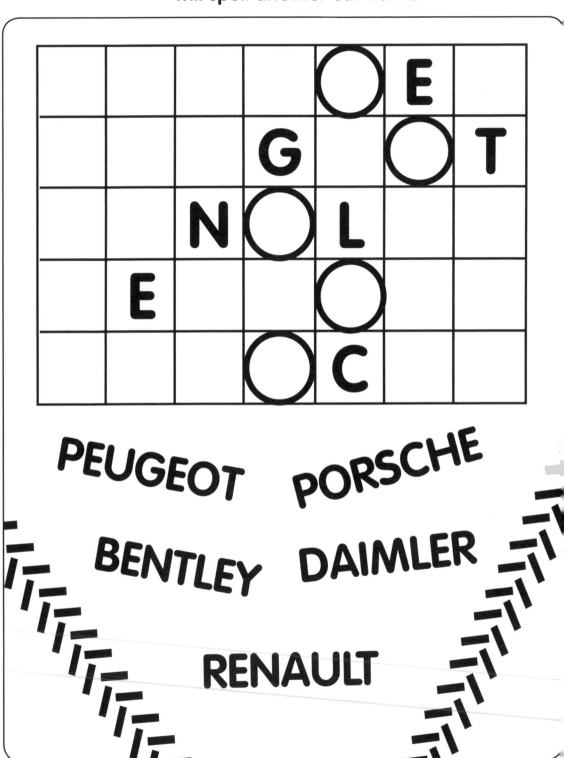

PEUGEOT   PORSCHE

BENTLEY   DAIMLER

RENAULT

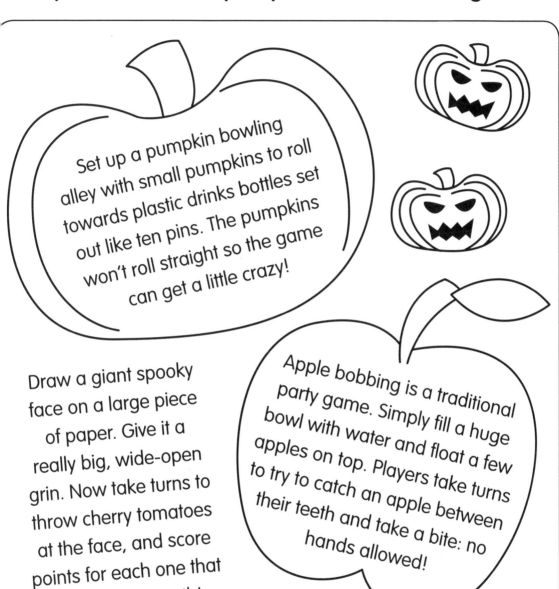

Set up a pumpkin bowling alley with small pumpkins to roll towards plastic drinks bottles set out like ten pins. The pumpkins won't roll straight so the game can get a little crazy!

Draw a giant spooky face on a large piece of paper. Give it a really big, wide-open grin. Now take turns to throw cherry tomatoes at the face, and score points for each one that goes in his mouth!

Apple bobbing is a traditional party game. Simply fill a huge bowl with water and float a few apples on top. Players take turns to try to catch an apple between their teeth and take a bite: no hands allowed!

Place a large pumpkin on the ground, and stand at least 4 metres back. Players take turns to throw kidney beans at the pumpkin, scoring a point every time their bean hits it. Keep score to see who wins.

120

These Archaeopteryx need colouring as they soar through the skies.

21 Write down every other letter, starting with A, to find the name of one of the biggest dinosaurs that ever lived.

‒ ‒ ‒ ‒ ‒ ‒ ‒ ‒ ‒ ‒ ‒ ‒ ‒ ‒ ‒ ‒ ‒

122 **Which of the steam trains has travelled the farthest?**
Add up the numbers for each to find out.

Which of these is the real Phantom of the Opera?
Use the clues to work it out.

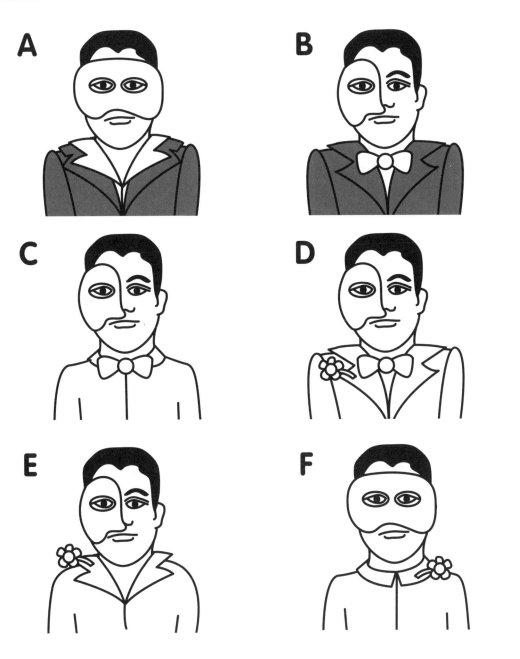

His mask covers only one eye.

He isn't wearing a black jacket.

He has a flower on his shirt.

He hasn't got a bow tie.

Quick! Come to the rescue with some top-notch colouring.

Can you turn WAND into CAPE by changing one letter at a time? Each change must use a real word. Use the clues to help you.

WAND

__ __ __ __   Hold your wand with it

__ __ __ __   Opposite of soft

__ __ __ __   Similar to a rabbit

__ __ __ __   Looking after something

CAPE

Which of these vehicles is the odd one out?

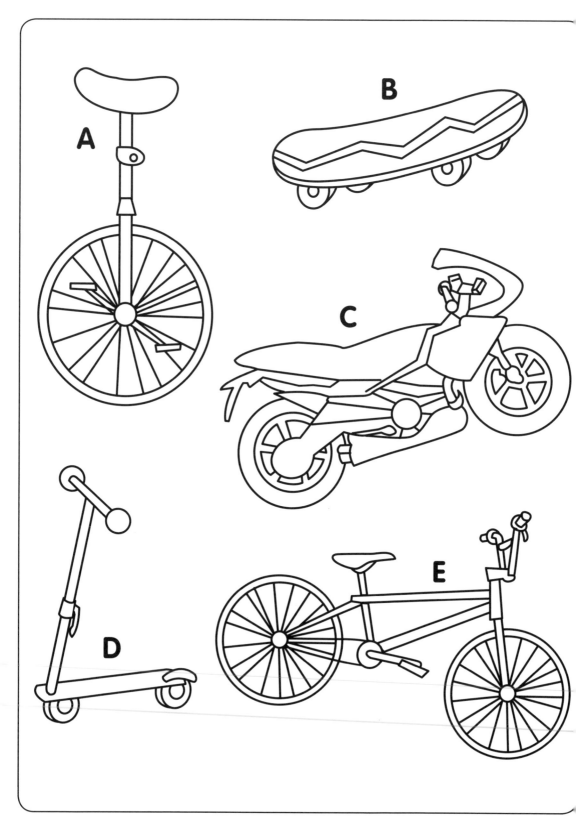

A

B

C

D

E

Cross out any letter that appears more than once to find the name of a type of vampire. It's a tricky one!

Watch out for Pachycephalosaurus' hard head as you colour him!

29 Match the squares to the main picture and write the correct grid reference for each one. One has been done to show you how.

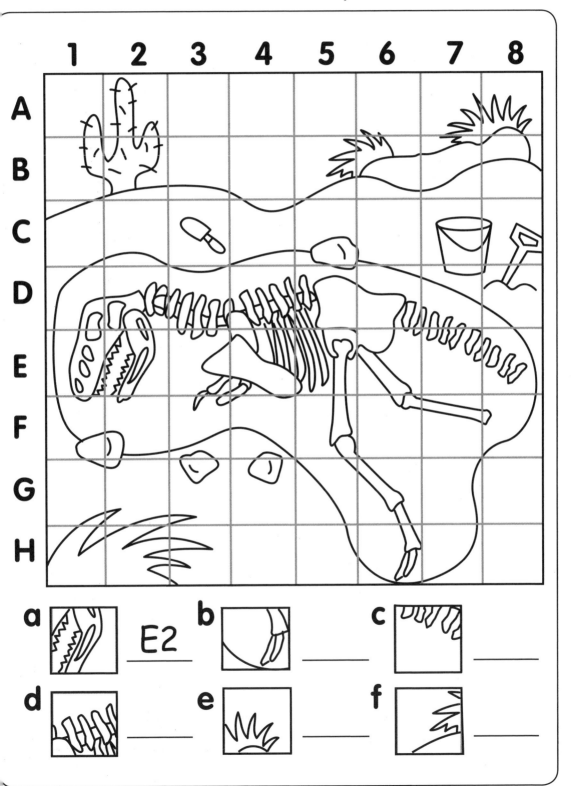

a E2

b ___

c ___

d ___

e ___

f ___

Can you spot six differences between these two pictures?

Which of these Iguanodons has the right answer to the sum 100 − 63 + 2.5 + 10.5 − 5 = ?

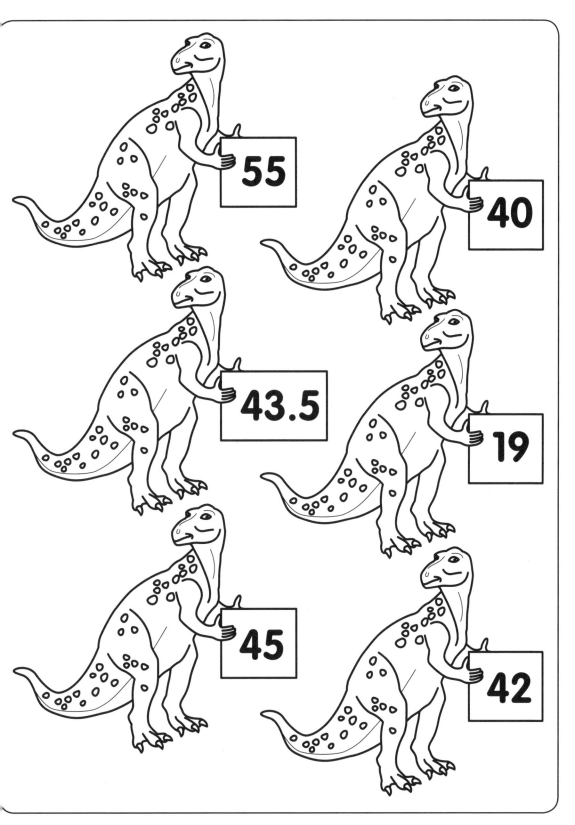

Have fun colouring these super-speedy race cars.

Follow the trail of creatures from cat to rat to bat
each time, and find a way to the witch at the end.

START

134 Can you fit each of these car companies into the wheel? The shaded spaces are the last letter of one word and the first letter of the next.

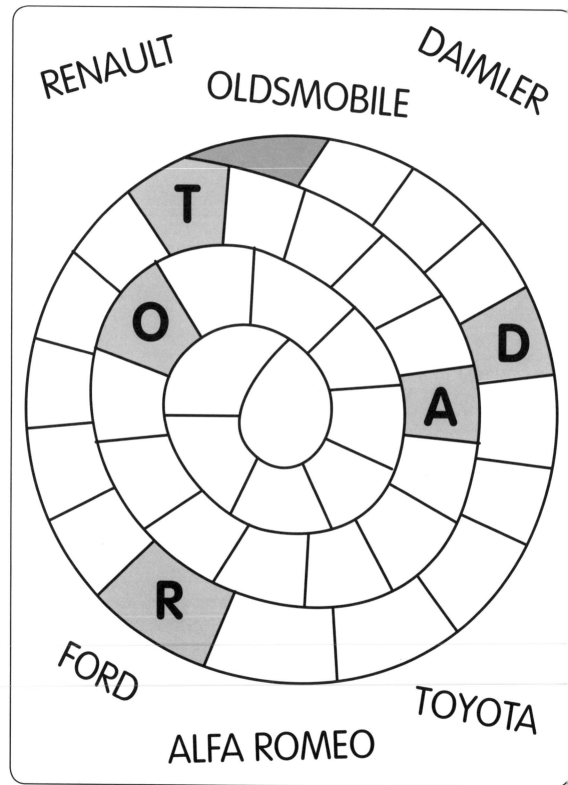

RENAULT

OLDSMOBILE

DAIMLER

FORD

TOYOTA

ALFA ROMEO

Which owl has flown the farthest through the forest?
Add up the numbers on each owl's path.

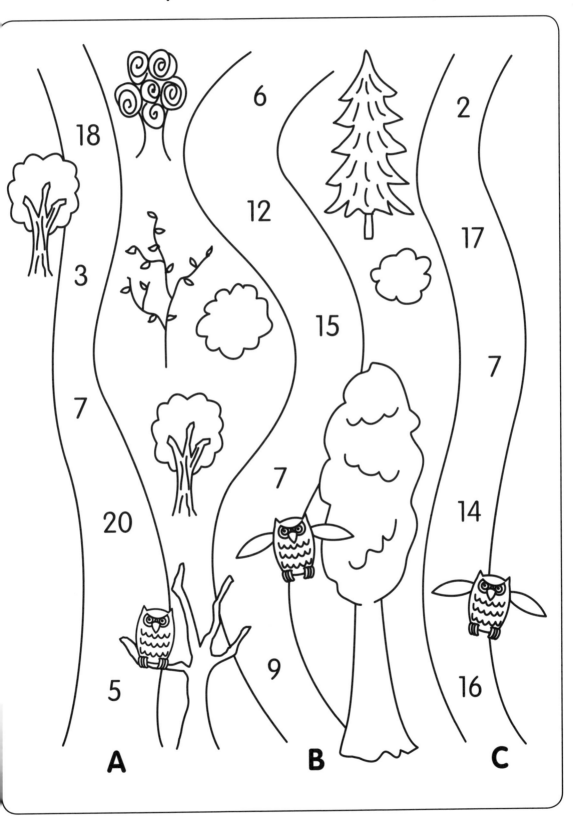

18

6

2

3

12

17

7

15

7

7

20

14

5

9

16

A

B

C

Colour in this mother Maiasaura and her nest of babies.

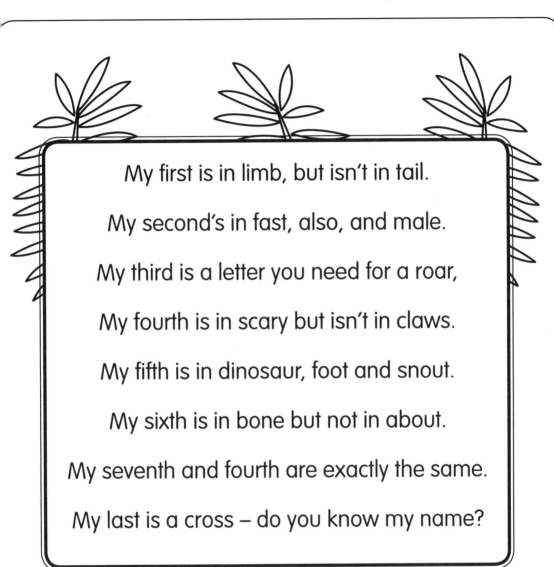

My first is in limb, but isn't in tail.

My second's in fast, also, and male.

My third is a letter you need for a roar,

My fourth is in scary but isn't in claws.

My fifth is in dinosaur, foot and snout.

My sixth is in bone but not in about.

My seventh and fourth are exactly the same.

My last is a cross – do you know my name?

How many broomsticks are piled up in this room?

Use the clues to work out the order the trucks come in their race.

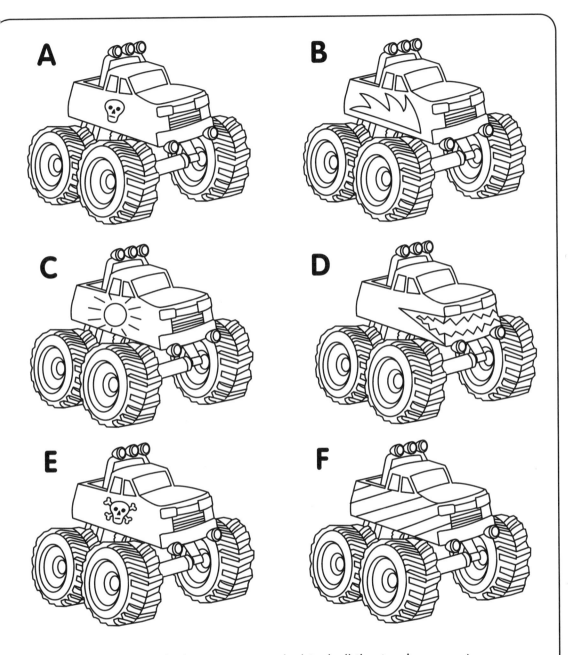

1. The truck with the sun comes behind all the trucks except one.
2. The striped truck has two trucks in front of it.
3. A truck with a skull is in second place.
4. The jaws truck is at least one ahead of the striped truck.
5. The skull and crossbones truck is ahead of the flames truck but behind the striped truck.

Draw your own scary characters to go with the ones here.

Race up the mountain maze to get to the cable car at the top.

START

Match up the plant eaters to the correct answer for each sum.

36

32

11 x 3

50 – 13

Half of 64

34

37

33

12 + 22

6 x 6

Start the countdown, and colour this rocket before it launches into space.

Pair up the boxes to make the names of eight fantastical or creepy creatures. One has already been done to help you.

DRA WIZ SPI ZOM

GOB ~~GOR~~ SPH MED

G O R G O N _ _ _ _ _ _

_ _ _ _ _ _ _ _ _ _ _ _

_ _ _ _ _ _ _ _ _ _ _ _

_ _ _ _ _ _ _ _ _ _ _ _

ARD DER LIN USA

BIE ~~GON~~

GON INX

45 Draw lines between Dr Jekyll's test tubes to link pairs of numbers that add up to 100. Get it right, or Mr Hyde will be unleashed!

Cross out every other letter, starting from X, to find something that helicopters are used for.

47 This Ankylosaurus is ready for battle – but you can add some colour first.

148 Baba Yaga is a famous character in Russian tales. She is a wicked old crone who lives in a hut that moves around on chicken legs! Study this picture for a few minutes and then cover the page to see how much you can remember.

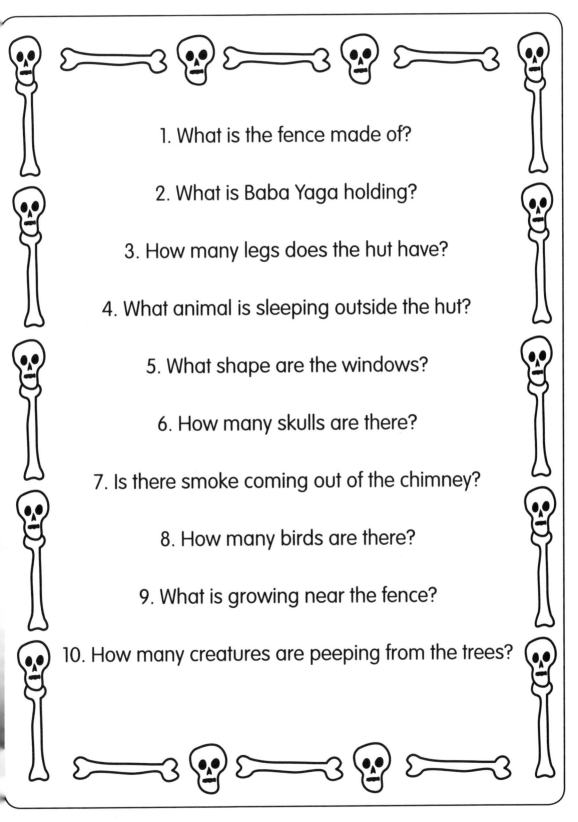

1. What is the fence made of?

2. What is Baba Yaga holding?

3. How many legs does the hut have?

4. What animal is sleeping outside the hut?

5. What shape are the windows?

6. How many skulls are there?

7. Is there smoke coming out of the chimney?

8. How many birds are there?

9. What is growing near the fence?

10. How many creatures are peeping from the trees?

150 Read the clues and put ticks in the boxes to work out which age each dinosaur lived in, and how tall they were.

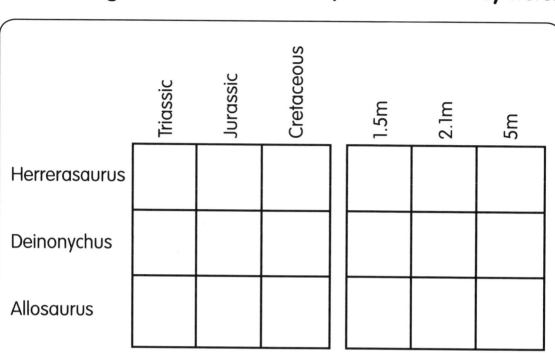

	Triassic	Jurassic	Cretaceous		1.5m	2.1m	5m
Herrerasaurus							
Deinonychus							
Allosaurus							

1. Herrerasaurus was around before the other two dinosaurs.

2. The Jurassic dinosaur was the tallest.

3. Deinonychus was shorter than the others.

4. Allosaurus lived before Deinonychus.

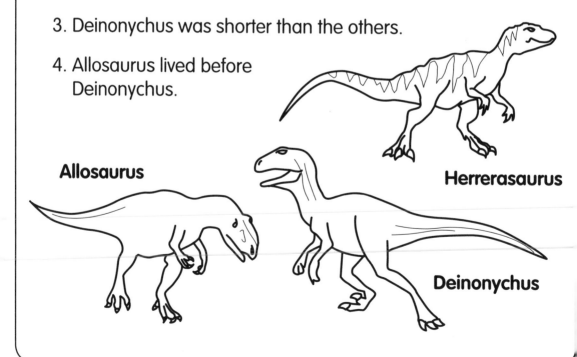

Allosaurus

Herrerasaurus

Deinonychus

**Brighten up this scene
with lots of colour.**

152

Only two of these vampires are the same.
Can you tell which two?

Uncode the symbols on this dinosaur's spikes to find out what it is called.

K E N T R O S A U R U S

A = ● I = ⌘ Q = ♈

B = ✡ J = ☒ R = ✓

C = ✋ K = ❖ S = ⊕

D = ⚑ L = ☢ T = ⇨

E = ☺ M = ○ U = ▲

F = ◆ N = ★ V = ❄

G = ✠ O = ☼ W = ✳

H = ☐ P = ⬤ X = ✳

154 Look at the main picture of the aircraft carrier and then work out which of the smaller pictures is how it would look from above.

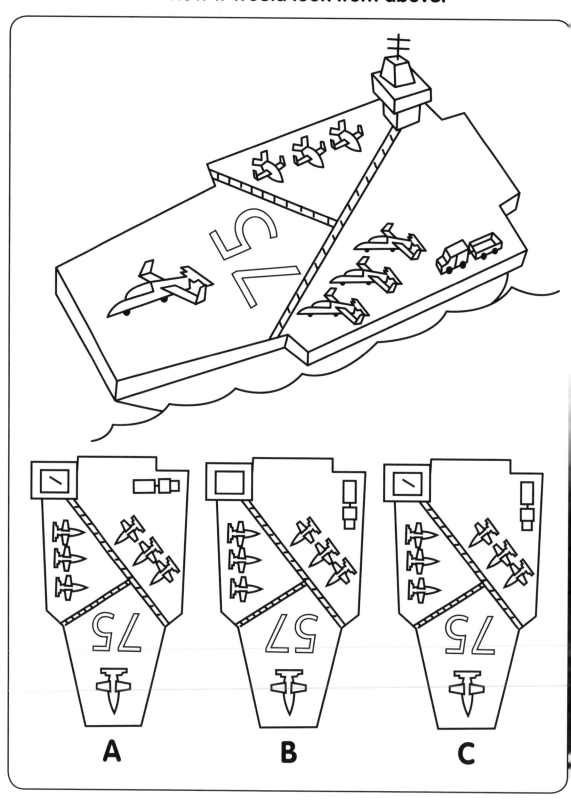

A

B

C

This Pterosaur is hunting for a snack.
What colour will you make him?

Which of the groups of letters cannot be unscrambled to spell BANSHEE correctly?

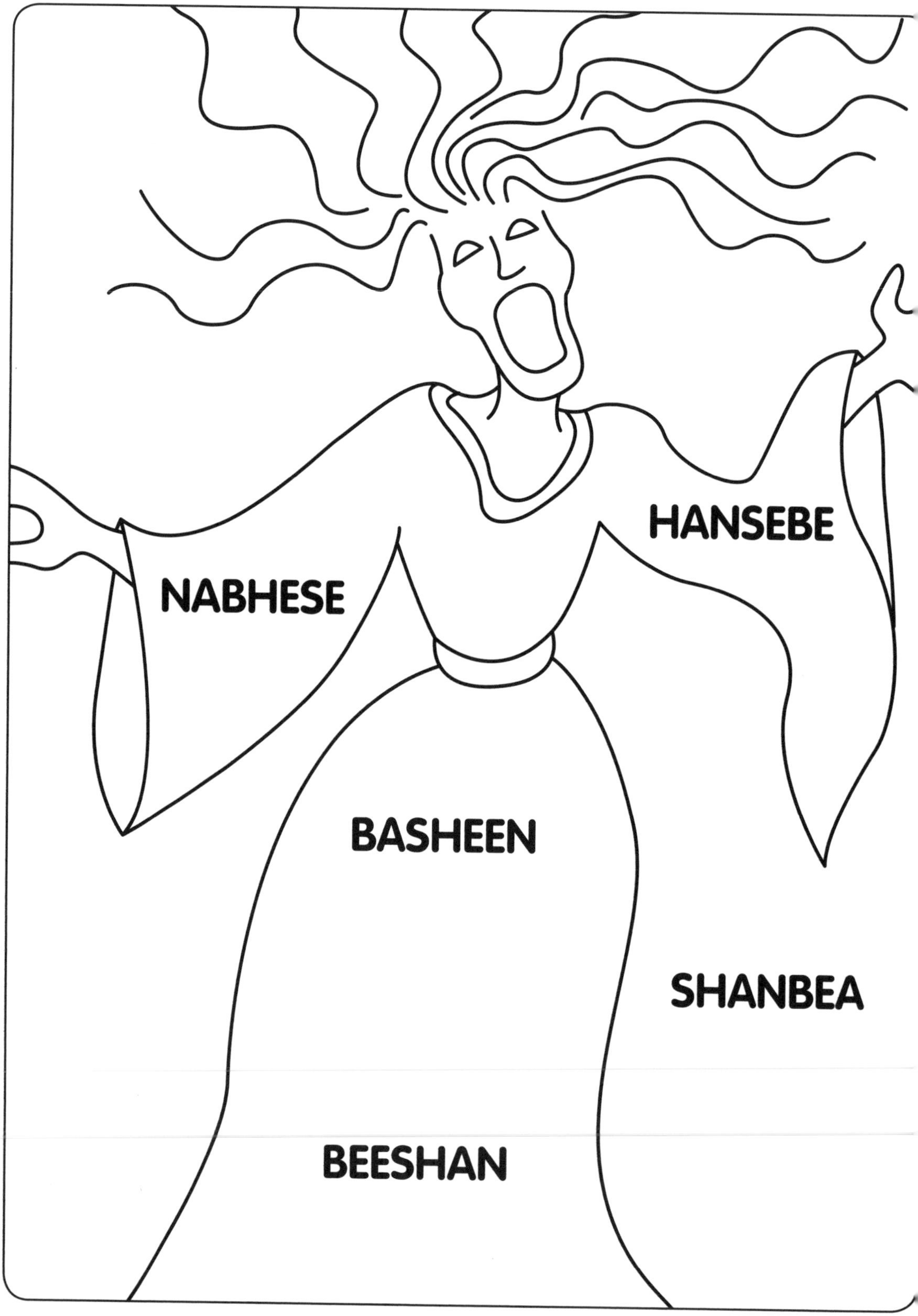

HANSEBE

NABHESE

BASHEEN

SHANBEA

BEESHAN

Can you spot eight differences between these Plesiosaur pictures?

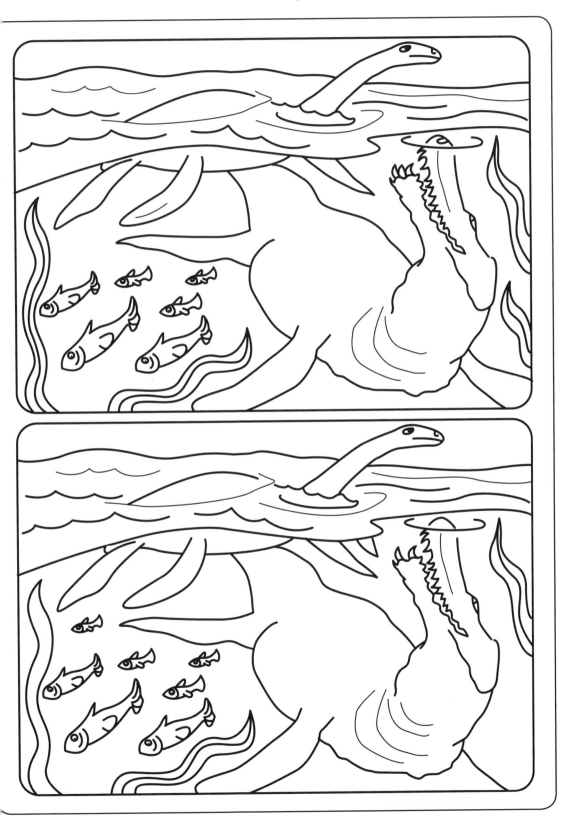

**Work out the sums in each serpent's crystal ball.
Try to do them without using a calculator.**

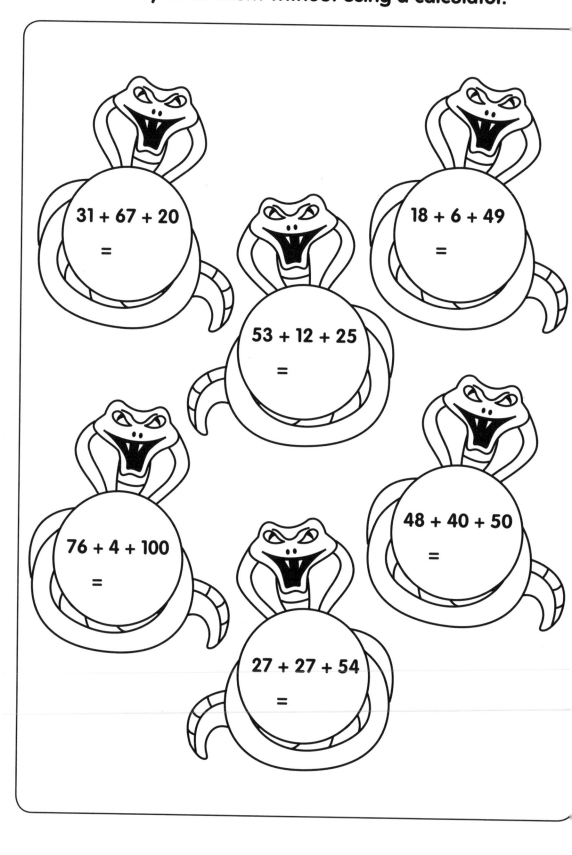

31 + 67 + 20
=

18 + 6 + 49
=

53 + 12 + 25
=

76 + 4 + 100
=

48 + 40 + 50
=

27 + 27 + 54
=

Colour the tractor with your favourite bright colour.

How many smaller words can you make from the letters below? Two are listed to get you started.

SHOUT

NUTS

Multiply two numbers next to each other to fill in the helmet of the rider above, like the example.

162 Fit each of the listed dinosaurs into the grid. The shaded squares are the last letter of one word and the first letter of the next.

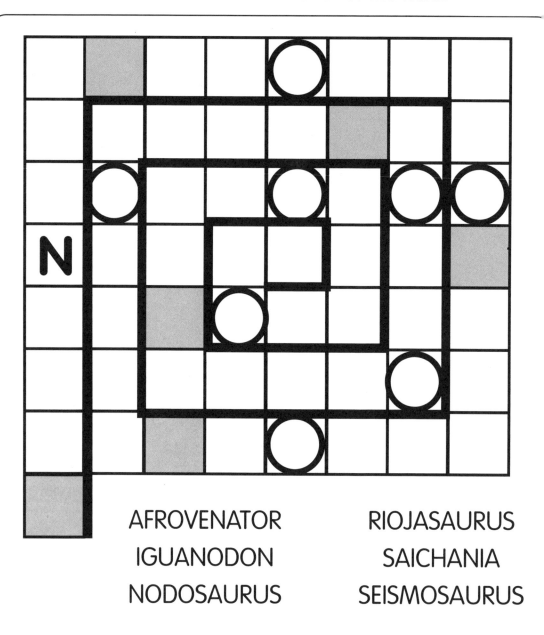

AFROVENATOR

IGUANODON

NODOSAURUS

RIOJASAURUS

SAICHANIA

SEISMOSAURUS

Now rearrange the circled letters to find
a word that describes Seismosaurus:

___ ___ ___ ___ ___ ___ ___ ___ ___ ___

Are you brave enough to colour the scary Spinosaurus?

Which of the silhouettes matches the main picture of the moon buggy?

Does it feel like these portraits are watching you? Add your own in the empty frames – draw members of your family or just make up some creepy characters.

Which of the hydra's heads does not match any of the others?

Use a different colour for each of the jets' trails if you like!

168

Solve the sudoku puzzle so that every row,
column and mini-grid has each of the four symbols.

Starting at C, find the listed dinosaur words in a continuous trail through the grid.

AFROVENATOR

BAGACERATOPS

MINMI

C	O	M	P	A	U	R	O
N	G	O	S	S	B	S	L
A	P	A	R	A	A	U	O
T	S	E	V	O	G	H	P
H	U	N	A	R	A	C	E
M	R	O	T	F	A	S	R
I	I	B	Y	O	N	P	A
N	M	A	R	X	Y	O	T

BARYONYX

PARASAUROLOPHUS

COMPSOGNATHUS

How many frightened creatures are hidden in this spooky forest?

Colour in this Apatosaurus as it munches on the leaves.

172 Use the clue letters to fit the names of the listed dinosaurs into the grid. The circled letters will spell another dinosaur for you.

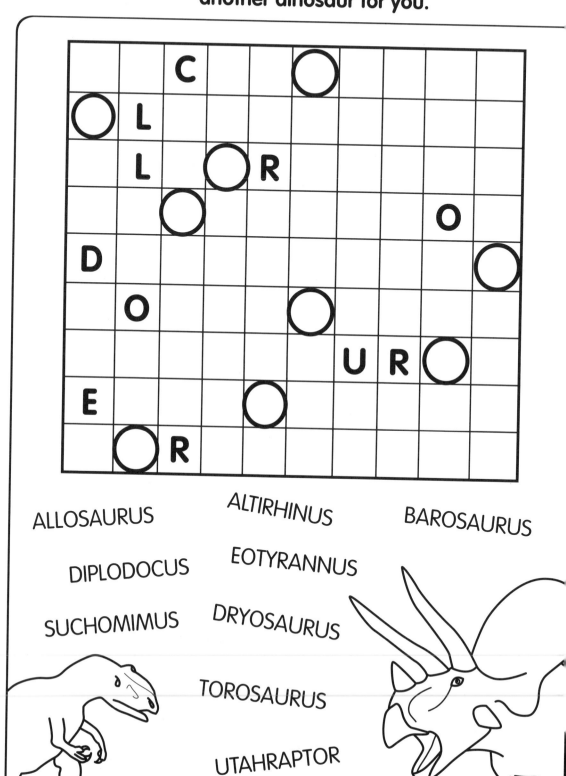

ALLOSAURUS

ALTIRHINUS

BAROSAURUS

DIPLODOCUS

EOTYRANNUS

SUCHOMIMUS

DRYOSAURUS

TOROSAURUS

UTAHRAPTOR

**Use the code to work out the
answer to this joke.**

What do you call an armoured dinosaur that's sleeping?

HGVTL-HMLIFH!

CODE

A	B	C	D	E	F	G	H	I	J	K	L	M	N
Z	**Y**	**X**	**W**	**V**	**U**	**T**	**S**	**R**	**Q**	**P**	**O**	**N**	**M**

O	P	Q	R	S	T	U	V	W	X	Y	Z
L	**K**	**J**	**I**	**H**	**G**	**F**	**E**	**D**	**C**	**B**	**A**

Guide the snowmobile through the snowdrifts to safety by choosing numbers from the five times table.

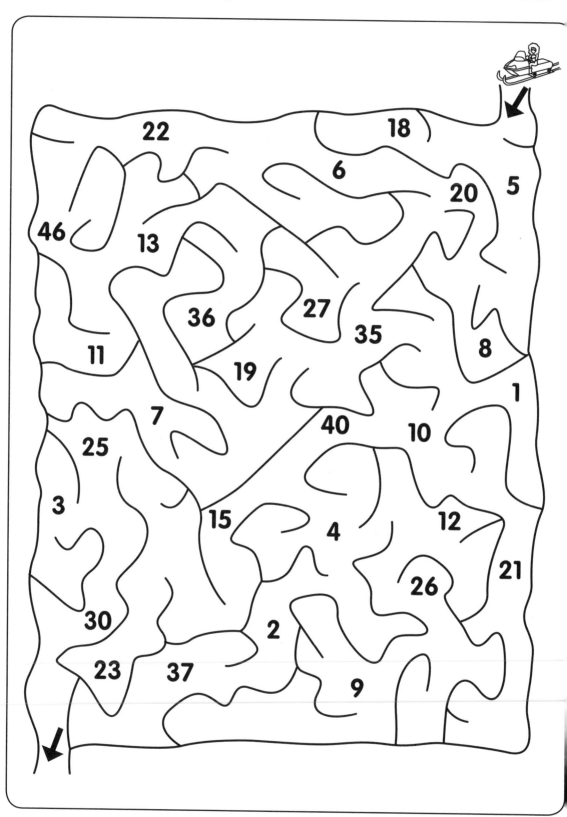

Add some colour for the drivers of these cars.

These dinosaurs all need labelling.
Can you match the names to the correct pictures?

Stegosaurus

Styracosaurus

Iguanodon

Ankylosaurus

T-rex

Which of the rockets has the highest mission number?
Do the sums to find out.

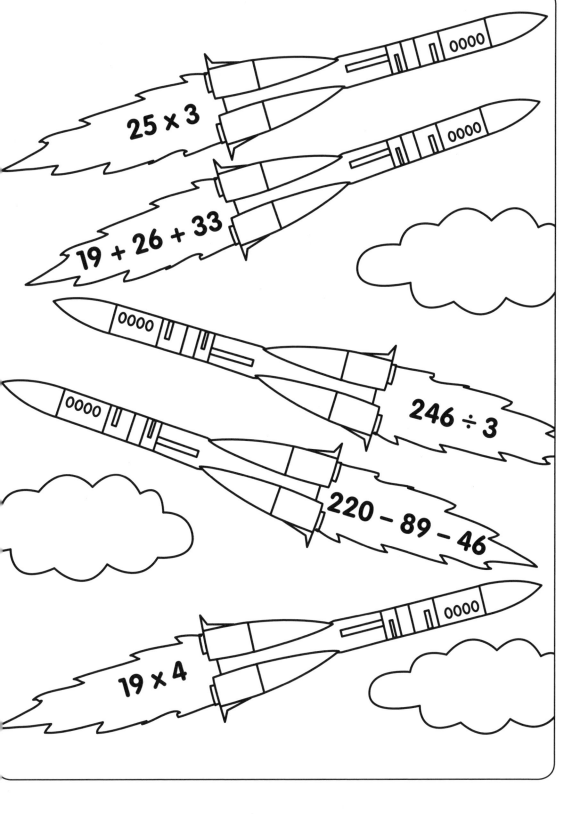

25×3

$19 + 26 + 33$

$246 \div 3$

$220 - 89 - 46$

19×4

Fill in the missing letters to complete the names of six scary movies. Rearrange the new letters to make another spooky word.

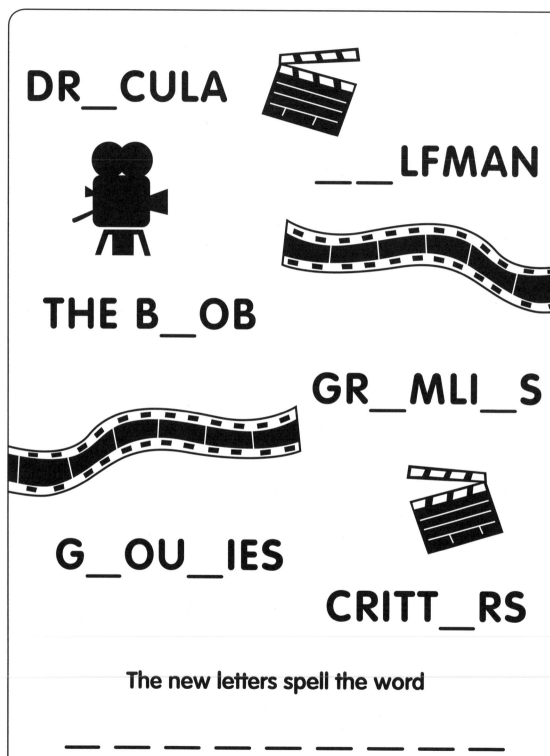

DR __ __ CULA

__ __ LFMAN

THE B __ __ OB

GR __ MLI __ S

G __ OU __ IES

CRITT __ RS

The new letters spell the word

__ __ __ __ __ __ __ __ __ __

79 Colour these dinosaurs to show
off their amazing patterns.

180 Can you find the ten listed words hidden in the grid?
They can appear up and down, diagonally, and
backwards or forwards.

```
b  y  e  l  p  l  s  c  r
s  a  s  w  a  l  n  e  h
c  h  s  c  r  e  a  m  o
r  d  r  w  a  y  r  l  w
e  y  d  i  c  u  i  l  l
e  h  o  w  e  a  J  a  c
c  o  v  b  w  k  l  a  c
h  k  r  e  l  l  o  h  f
s  h  r  l  t  u  o  h  s
```

cry	screech
scream	shriek
shout	wail
holler	yell
howl	yelp

See if you can solve these maths problems without a calculator.

Libby is at the Dinosaur Museum shop. She has £5 and wants to buy a book that costs £2.50 and a poster that costs £3.50. Does she have enough money?

There are 30 people in Libby's class.
They need to split into 6 work groups.
How many children will be
in each group?

Half of Libby's class are boys. Five of the boys don't like dinosaurs. How many boys do like dinosaurs?

The class are at the museum from 10 o'clock until 2 o'clock. How much time do they have there?

If they have half an hour for lunch and one hour in a dino talk, how long do they have left to look around?

  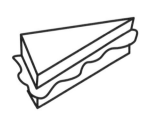

Which of the jigsaw pieces completes the picture?

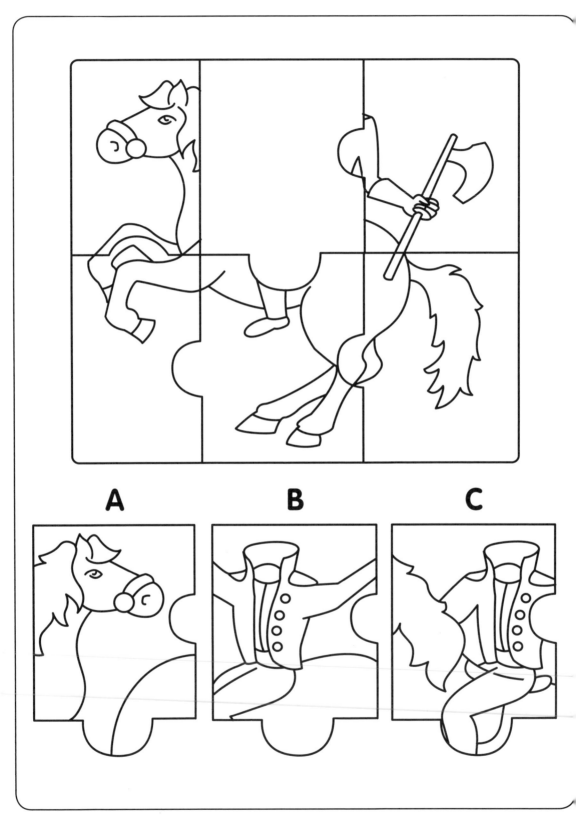

A

B

C

What load does the tractor need to collect? Cross out any letter that appears twice and use the remaining letters to spell a word.

184

This mummy is on the rampage!
But which silhouette matches him exactly?

85

This chopper is off on a road trip.
Add your own custom designs!

How many smaller words can you make from the letters below? Two are listed to get you started.

CRETACEOUS PERIOD

POST

CREASE

Can you spot eight differences between these two pictures?

188 How many ammonites are swimming here?
And can you spot a tiny trilobite amongst them?

What colour do you want the Stegosaurus's spikes to be?

Follow the instructions to find the answer to the joke.

What did the traffic light say to the car?

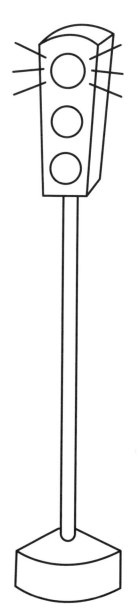

BRAIN	STOP	SHUT
WE'LL	DON'T	DRIVE
SOON	BE	TRAIN
LOOK	CRANE	I'M
MAIN	NEAR	SAFE
CHANGING	STATION	HELP

1. Cross out words beginning with S.

2. Delete words that rhyme with 'rain'.

3. Get rid of any word containing E.

If A=1, B=2, C=3 and so on, work out which dinosaur name is in each giant footprint.

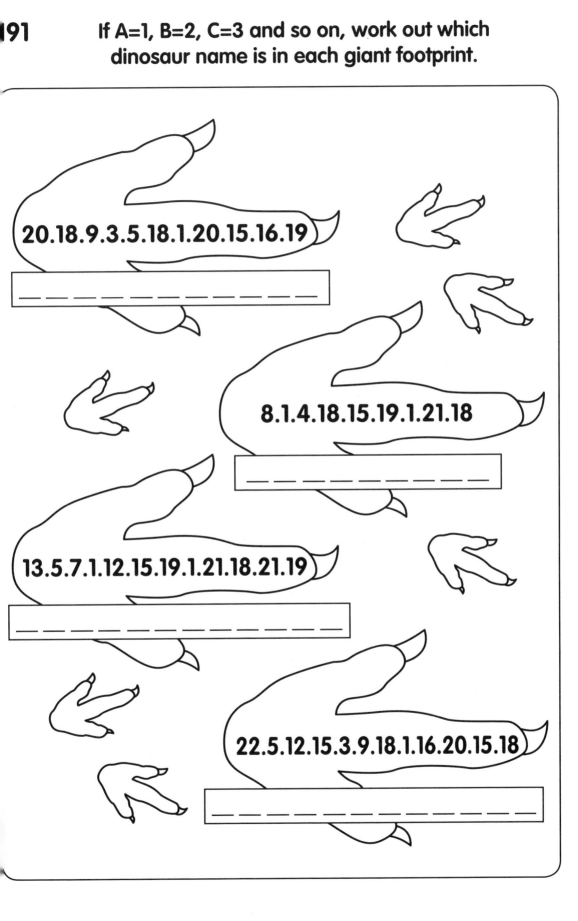

20.18.9.3.5.18.1.20.15.16.19

_ _ _ _ _ _ _ _ _ _ _ _

8.1.4.18.15.19.1.21.18

_ _ _ _ _ _ _ _ _ _ _

13.5.7.1.12.15.19.1.21.18.21.19

_ _ _ _ _ _ _ _ _ _ _ _

22.5.12.15.3.9.18.1.16.20.15.18

_ _ _ _ _ _ _ _ _ _ _ _

192 Find your way to the finish line following the symbols helmet-wheel-warning triangle in that order each time.

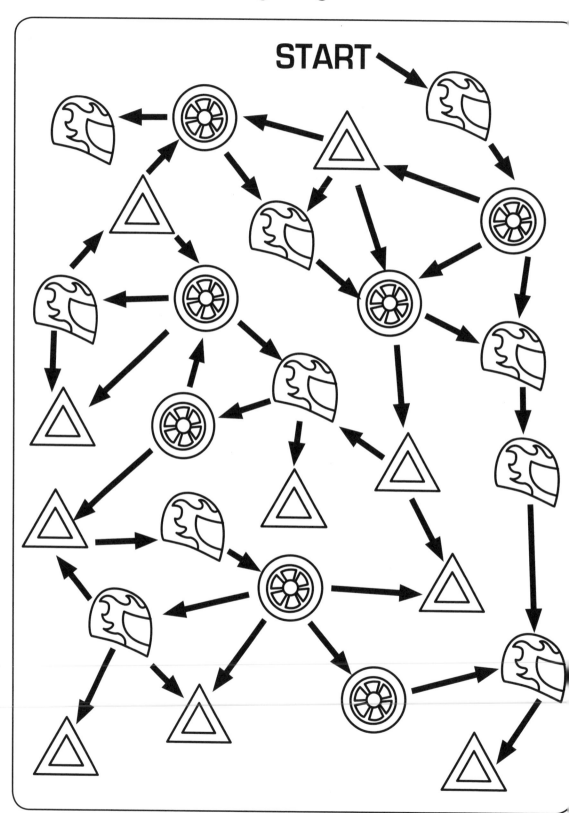

These Chinese dragons all look the same, but only two of them are identical. Can you spot which two?

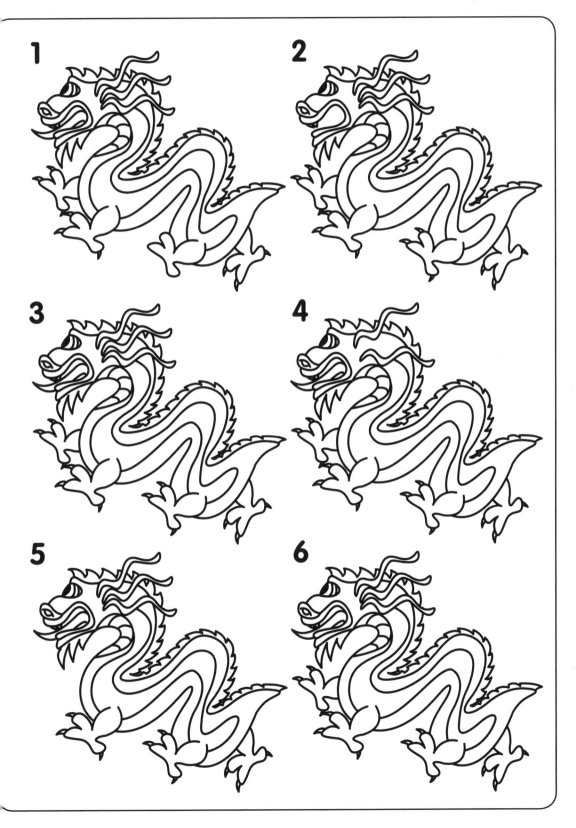

This game needs to be prepared in advance, but is brilliant fun! It's best for a party at a house, with a handful of guests. Play it in one room, or set it up between two or three rooms for extra mayhem.

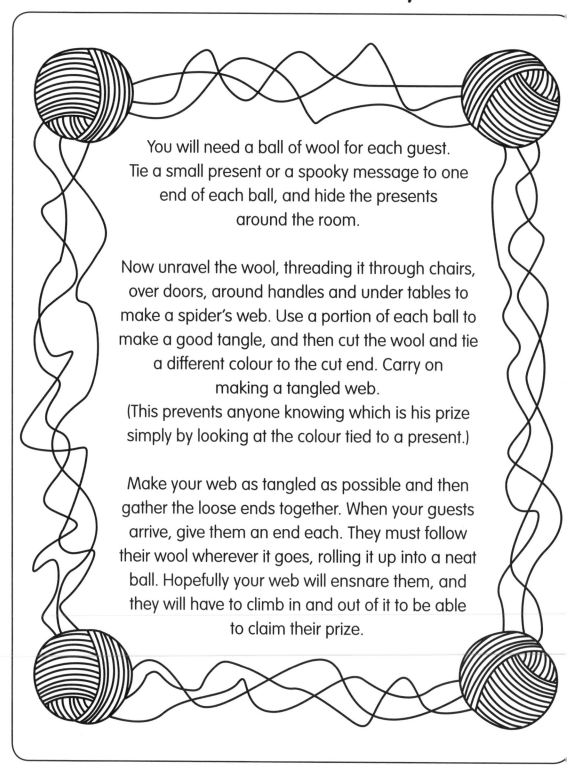

You will need a ball of wool for each guest. Tie a small present or a spooky message to one end of each ball, and hide the presents around the room.

Now unravel the wool, threading it through chairs, over doors, around handles and under tables to make a spider's web. Use a portion of each ball to make a good tangle, and then cut the wool and tie a different colour to the cut end. Carry on making a tangled web.
(This prevents anyone knowing which is his prize simply by looking at the colour tied to a present.)

Make your web as tangled as possible and then gather the loose ends together. When your guests arrive, give them an end each. They must follow their wool wherever it goes, rolling it up into a neat ball. Hopefully your web will ensnare them, and they will have to climb in and out of it to be able to claim their prize.

Add your best camouflage colours to these army vehicles.

Cross out any C, M or N. The remaining letters spell a common link between the pictured dinosaurs.

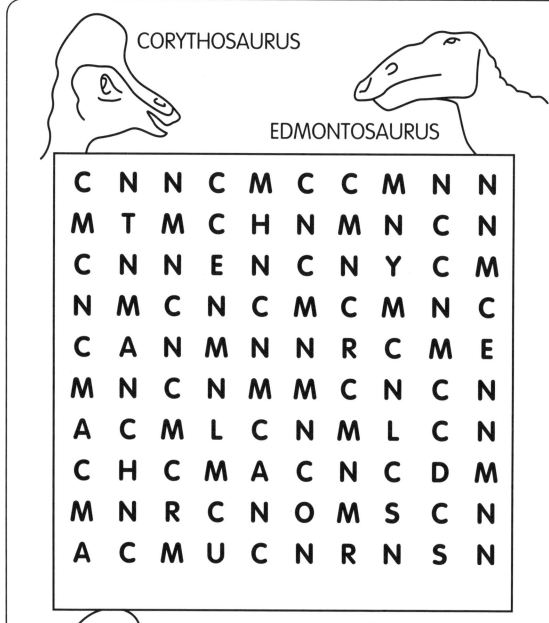

CORYTHOSAURUS

EDMONTOSAURUS

C	N	N	C	M	C	C	M	N	N
M	T	M	C	H	N	M	N	C	N
C	N	N	E	N	C	N	Y	C	M
N	M	C	N	C	M	C	M	N	C
C	A	N	M	N	N	R	C	M	E
M	N	C	N	M	M	C	N	C	N
A	C	M	L	C	N	M	L	C	N
C	H	C	M	A	C	N	C	D	M
M	N	R	C	N	O	M	S	C	N
A	C	M	U	C	N	R	N	S	N

PARASAUROLOPHUS

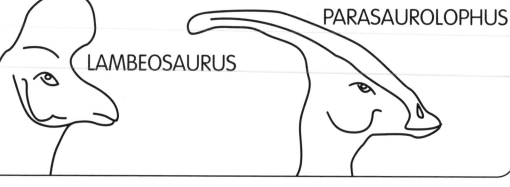

LAMBEOSAURUS

Join the dots to find out what kind of dinosaur is hiding.

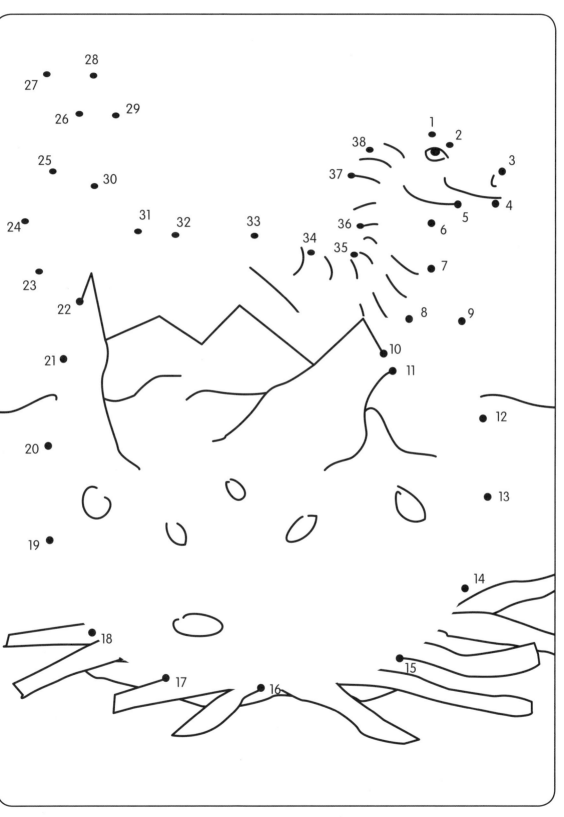

Cross out every other letter, starting with P,
to find out what has made these tracks.

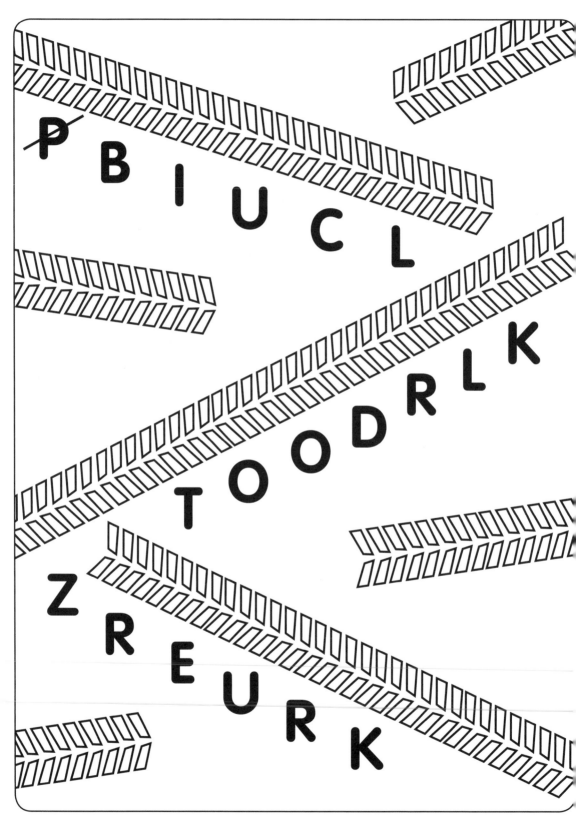

Watch out - this T-rex looks hungry.
Colour him in, quick!

If A=1, B=2, C=3 and so on, work out what letters are in each cauldron to spell disgusting potion ingredients.

Cauldron 1: 4 18 1 7 15 14 / 12 9 22 5 18

Cauldron 2: 2 1 20 / 2 12 15 15 4

Cauldron 3: 20 15 1 4 / 23 1 18 20 19

Cauldron 4: 19 12 21 7 / 19 12 9 13 5

Use the letters on the trilobites swimming to the right to spell the name of someone who is very interested in dinosaurs.

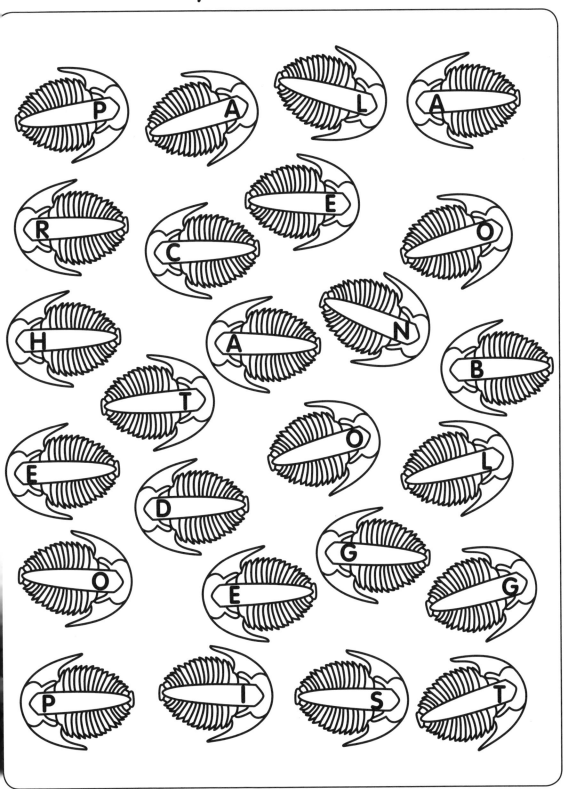

Which of these camper vans is not exactly the same as the others?

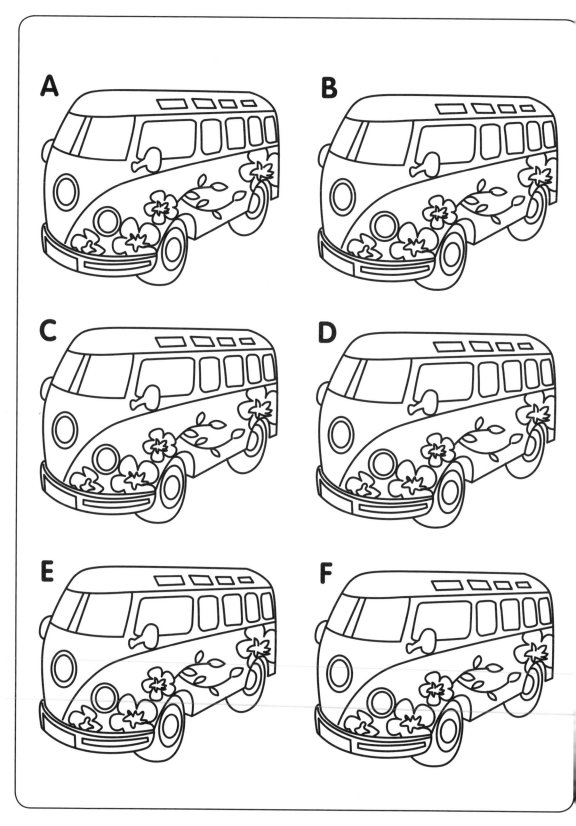

A

B

C

D

E

F

03 Fit the three-letter words into the spaces to finish
the names of four carnivorous dinosaurs.

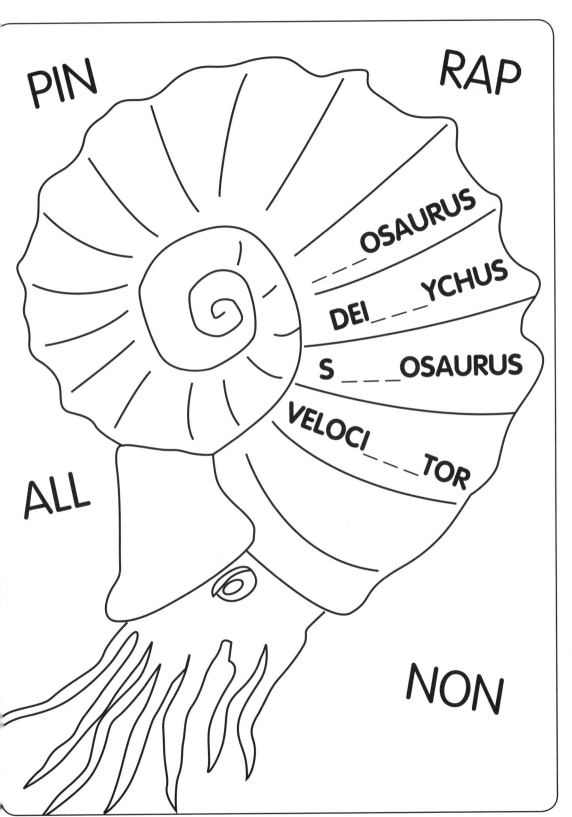

PIN

RAP

____OSAURUS

DEI____YCHUS

S ____OSAURUS

VELOCI____TOR

ALL

NON

Study the sequence of pictures carefully
and work out which of the monsters
finishes the pattern: A, B or C?

A   B   C

Colour in this old fashioned ship as it sails the high seas.

206

This jigsaw is of a Giganotosaurus!
Which of the three pieces finished the picture?

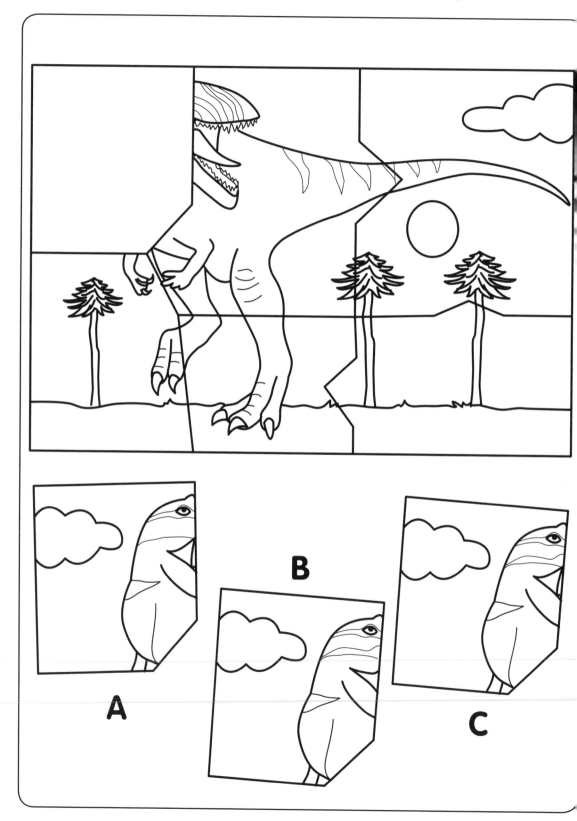

A

B

C

Solve the sums and use any answers that are odd numbers to travel across the herd of Hypsilophodon.

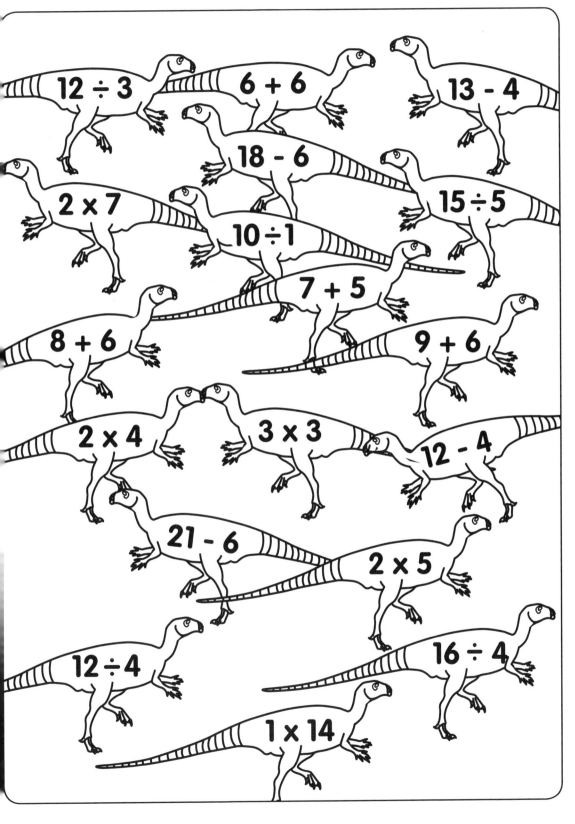

$12 \div 3$

$6 + 6$

$13 - 4$

$18 - 6$

2×7

$15 \div 5$

$10 \div 1$

$7 + 5$

$8 + 6$

$9 + 6$

2×4

3×3

$12 - 4$

$21 - 6$

2×5

$12 \div 4$

$16 \div 4$

1×14

208

Which of these racing cars does not pass the chequered flag?

Fill the feathers of this Caudipteryx in bright colours.

Styracosaurus had long sharp horns on its head – watch out! Which silhouette matches the main picture?

211 Only two of these bikes are identical.
Can you see which two?

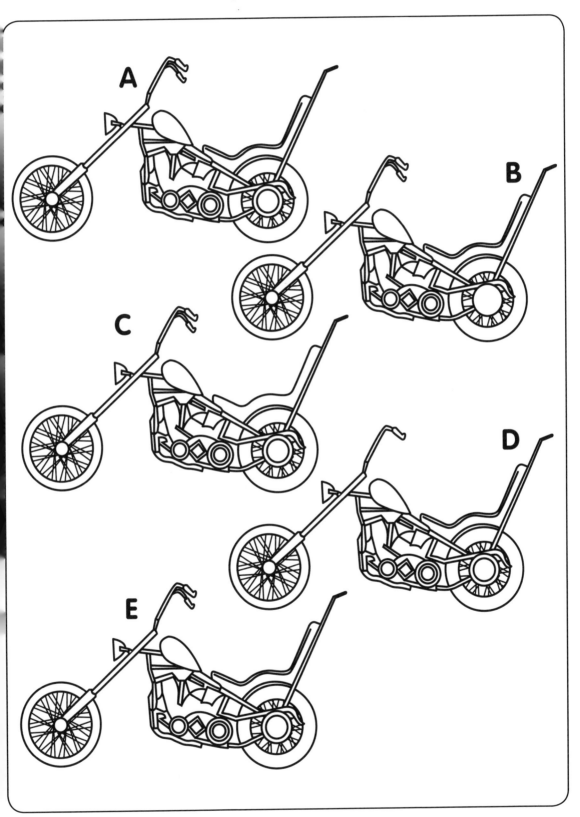

212 Can you fit each of the listed words back into the spiral of doom? The framed spaces are the last letter of one word and the first letter of the next.

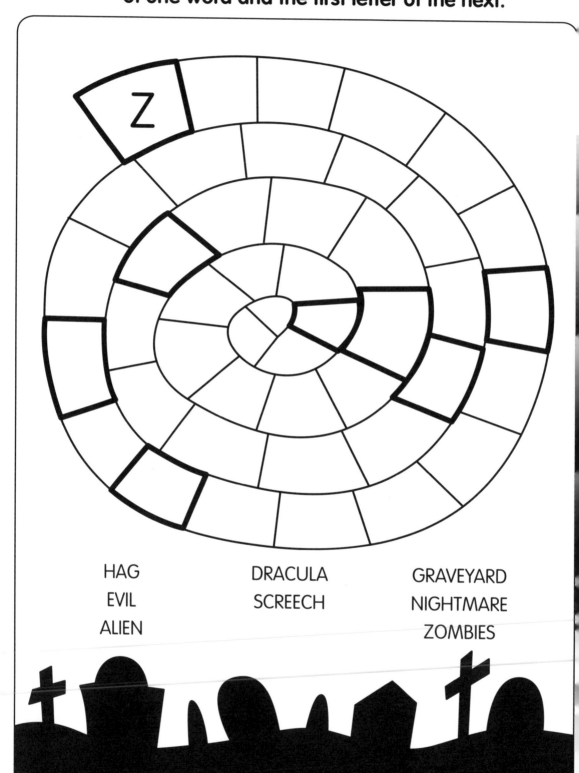

HAG	DRACULA	GRAVEYARD
EVIL	SCREECH	NIGHTMARE
ALIEN		ZOMBIES

Which of the numbers on this mighty Torosaurus are NOT in the eight times table?

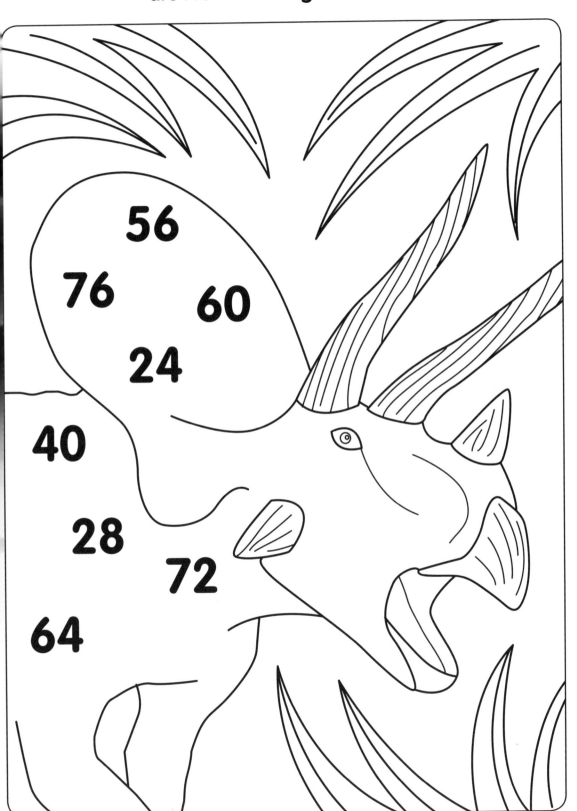

56

76

60

24

40

28

72

64

Follow the instructions to find out where each train listed on the timetable below is travelling to.

Write down the two letters shown by the minute hand, then the two letters shown by the hour hand. This will give you a four-letter word, for example, OHIO.

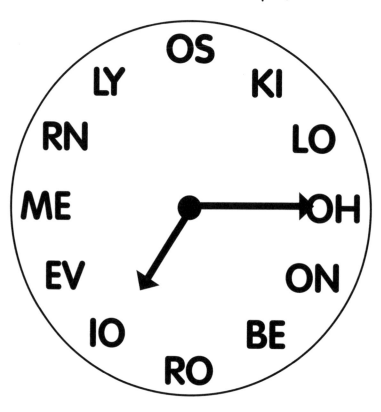

1. Half past nine.

2. Five past eight.

3. Two o'clock.

4. Twenty five past ten.

5. Five to four.

215 Can you find your way from the head to the feet of this Massospondylus maze?

Can you spot eight differences between these two pictures?

Which two of these Ankylosaurus are the same?

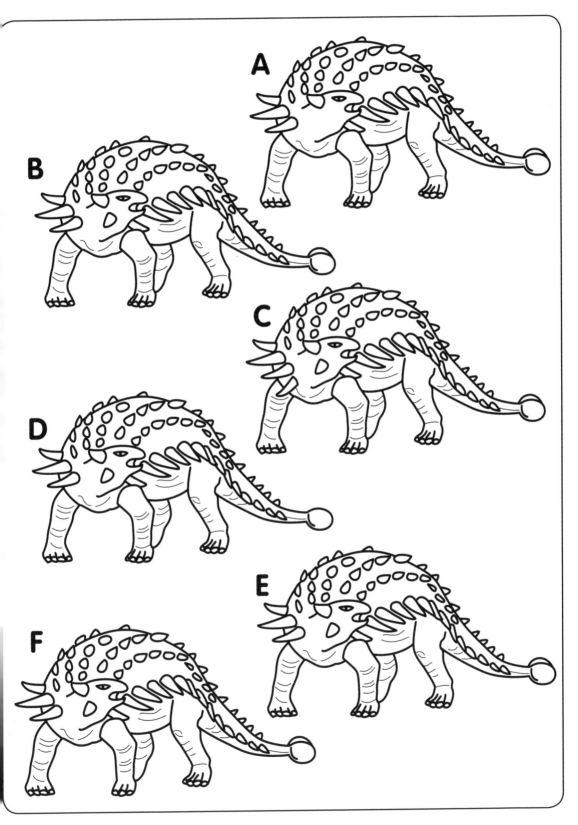

What message is written in the Evil Queen's magic mirror? Can you work it out?

Can you find all ten listed words hidden in the grid?

```
O S S J U R A S S I C O
P R E H I S T O R I C L
R E T E P A S S I C R O
E H E R X P R E D E E N
F J P A S T E R P T T T
P U R C S S I T P A A E
R R E R O V I N R A C R
E F S I T L B C C R E T
D C O S E H S I F T O S
A A H S H X I S V O U S
T R I A S S I C T O S O
O E R O V I B R E H R F
R C A R N I L J U R A E
C R E T I L E P R E D V
```

CARNIVORE   CRETACEOUS   EXTINCT

FOSSIL   HERBIVORE

JURASSIC   PREDATOR   PREHISTORIC

REPTILE   TRIASSIC

This Tenontosaurus is hungry! Circle the sums that have ten as the answer.

$100 \div 10$

$4\frac{1}{2} + 6\frac{1}{2}$

$3\frac{1}{2} + 6\frac{1}{2}$

$18 - 10$

$88 - 78$

$20 \div 10$

5×2

2×6

Which two pictures are exactly the same?

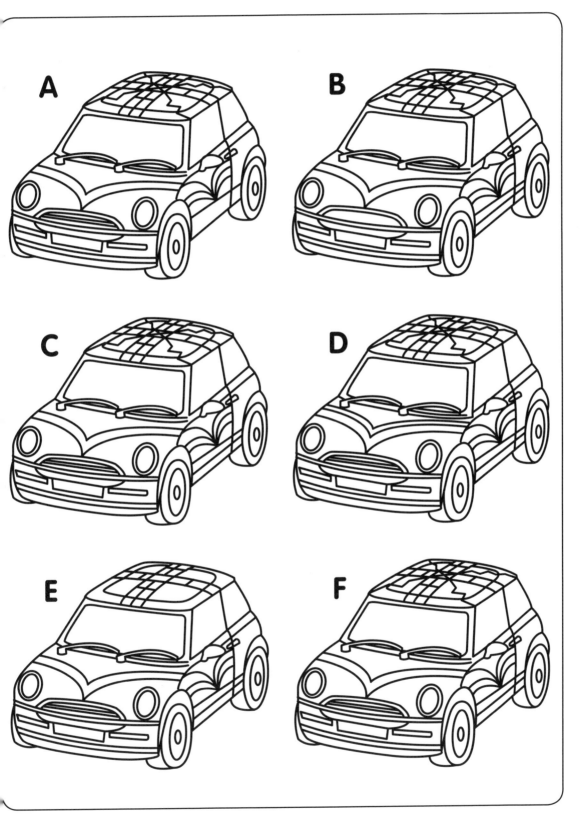

A

B

C

D

E

F

222

Double the number each time to fill in the spaces on T-rex's teeth.

Join the dots to find a highly unusual form of transport!

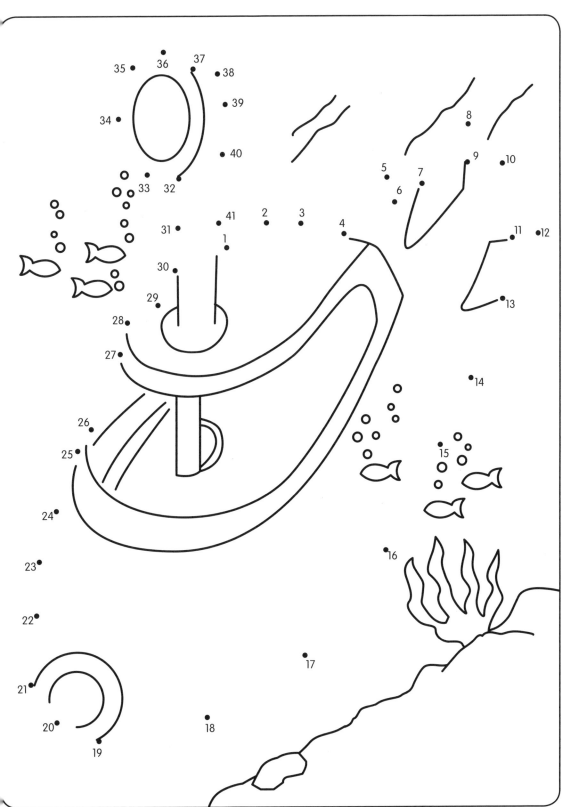

224 Use the clue letters to fit the dino-names into the grid. The circled letters will spell another dinosaur for you.

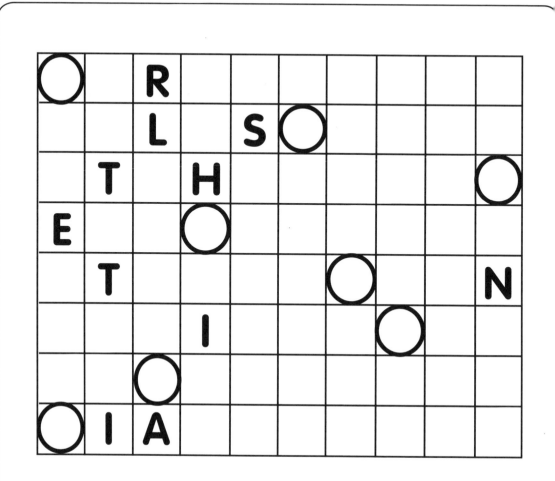

ALLOSAURUS   ALTIRHINUS

BAROSAURUS   DRYOSAURUS

EOTYRANNUS   PTERANODON

UTAHRAPTOR   XIAOSAURUS

25

How many Quetzalcoatlus are there skimming across this page?

ANSWERS

1.

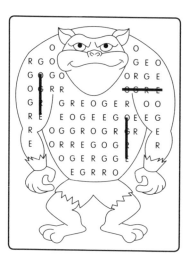

2. D

3. 810, 1136, 770, 851

4.

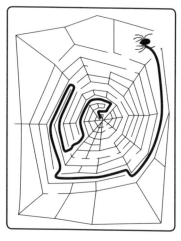

7.
1. Bottom
2. 3
3. Right
4. 4
5. All of them!
6. 2
7. Left
8. 2

8.

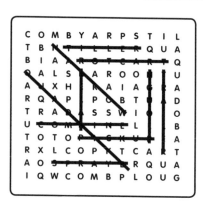

9. B

10.

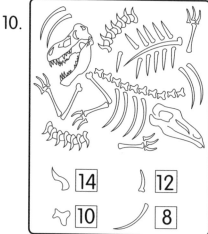

14   12
10   8

12. B

13.

14   1) serpent
    2) suspect
    3) sandpit
    4) slowest
    5) student
    6) scarlet
    7) servant
    8) sawdust
    9) soloist
    10) subject

16. Mike has a blue skateboard.
    Kate has a red bike.
    Sue has an orange scooter.

18.

19.

20. 7 14 21 28 35 42 49 56 63 70

22. B and F

23.

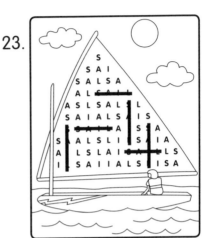

24.

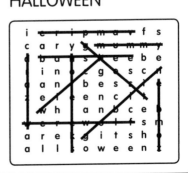

26. The hidden message is:
    IF SCARY BEINGS CAN BE
    SEEN, CHANCES ARE IT'S
    HALLOWEEN

28.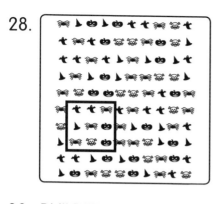

30. BUILDER

32. 1. ANKYLOSAURUS
    2. KENTROSAURUS
    3. PINACOSAURUS

33. 1. 150 km
    2. 28 litres
    3. 200 kph
    4. 10 Porsches
    5. 9 red

34. WOLF-WOOF-WOOD-MOOD-
    MOON

36. E

37.

38. 541 + 245 = 786
    123 + 135 = 258
    263 + 356 = 619
    421 + 246 = 667

40. SHADOW; GHOST; HAUNT

41. 150 + 850 = 1000
    350 + 650 = 1000
    250 + 750 = 1000
    450 + 550 = 1000

43. A = 1
    B = 3
    C = 2

44. IT WAS A TRICERAHOPS

45. 1st = black stripes
    2nd = checks
    3rd = black bonnet
    4th = grey
    5th = star

46.
```
        90
      40  50
   18  22  28
  8  10  12  16
 3   5   5   7   9
2  1  4  1  6  3
```

47. SEAPLANE

49.
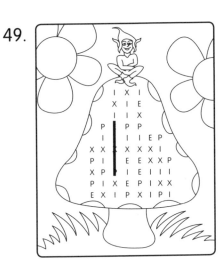

50. D

52. 15 bones, 6 skulls

53. A

54. Ferrari, Citroen, McLaren, Renault, Hyundai

56.
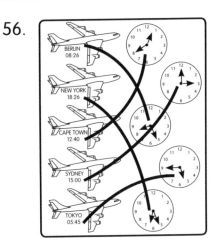

57. Here are some you might have thought of: jet, job, wet, brew, herb, where, threw, wreck, object, ejector.

58. 5941

60.
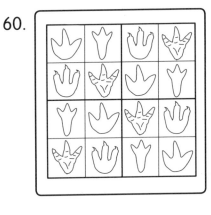

61. MONACO

63. $140 \div 4 = 35$
$\frac{1}{2} \times 56 = 28$
$36 - 4.5 = 31.5$

64.

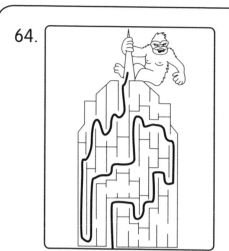

65. CARNOTAURUS

67.

68.

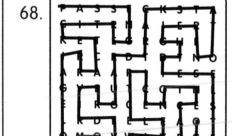

70. Hayley is going to Vienna for £120.
Lewis is going to Paris for £100.
Otto is going to Milan for £70.

71. TROODON

72.

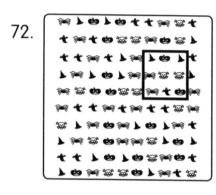

75. BRONTOSAURUS

76. Here are some you might have thought of: chef, quad, leg, red, queer, gel, reel, reef, herd, gale.

78.

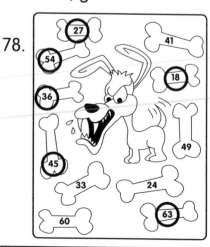

79.

80.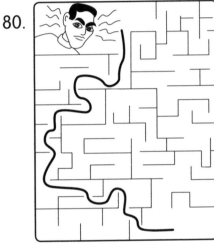

81. 3 7 10 17 27 44 71 115 186

82. D

84. 20 – 8 + 1 = 13

85. SHINKANSEN

86.

87. SPIDER web, web SITE
FUNNY bone, bone DRY
BLACK magic, magic SPELL
CANDLE stick, stick INSECT
DRAGON fly, fly FISHING
FULL moon, moon BEAM

88. C

90. 85 – 23 = 62
99 – 42 = 57
48 ÷ 8 = 6
44 + 33 = 77
5 x 12 = 60
56 + 44 = 100

92. 77 ÷ 7 = 11
63 ÷ 9 = 7
48 ÷ 6 = 8
42 ÷ 7 = 6
90 ÷ 10 = 9
15 ÷ 3 = 5

93. GASTASEURUS

94.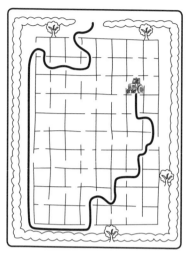

101.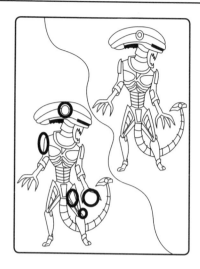

103. C

96. B, D, E, F, A, C

104. B and D

97.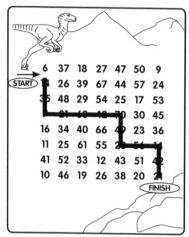

105.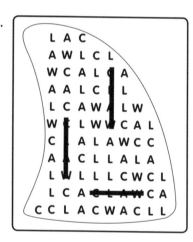

98. C

107. COMBINE

100. TRAP

108.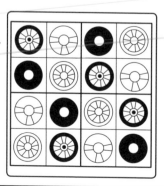

109. D

110.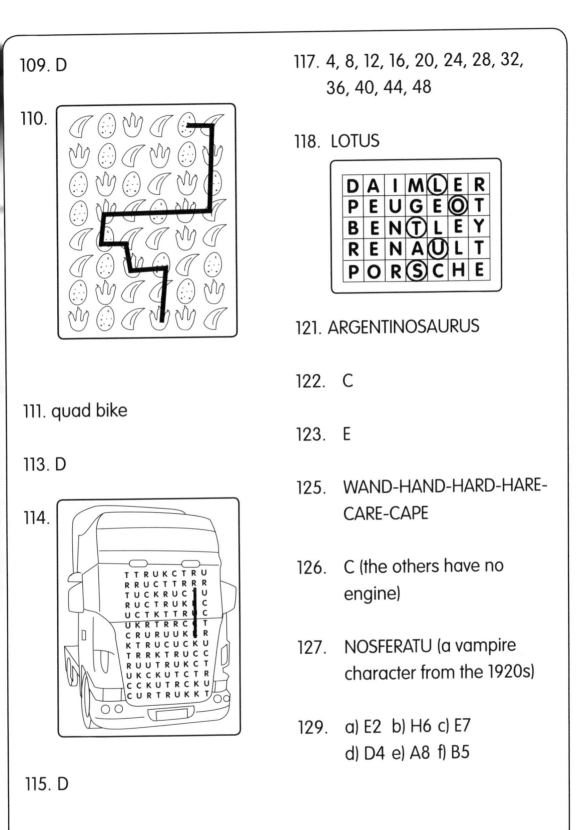

111. quad bike

113. D

114.

115. D

117. 4, 8, 12, 16, 20, 24, 28, 32, 36, 40, 44, 48

118. LOTUS

D	A	I	M	(L)	E	R
P	E	U	G	E	(O)	T
B	E	N	(T)	L	E	Y
R	E	N	A	(U)	L	T
P	O	R	(S)	C	H	E

121. ARGENTINOSAURUS

122. C

123. E

125. WAND-HAND-HARD-HARE-CARE-CAPE

126. C (the others have no engine)

127. NOSFERATU (a vampire character from the 1920s)

129. a) E2 b) H6 c) E7
     d) D4 e) A8 f) B5

130.

131. 45

133.

134. FORD-DAIMLER-RENAULT-
TOYOTA-ALFA ROMEO-OLD-
SMOBILE

135. C

137. BARYONYX

138. 12

139. 1st = D, then A, F, E, C, B

141.

142. 11 x 3 = 33
50 – 13 = 37
Half of 64 = 32
12 + 22 = 34
6 x 6 = 36

144. GORGON
DRAGON
GOBLIN
WIZARD
SPIDER
SPHINX
ZOMBIE
MEDUSA

145. 58 + 42 = 100
67 + 33 = 100
76 + 24 = 100
15 + 85 = 100

146. FIREFIGHTING

149. 1. Bones with skulls on
2. A broom
3. Two
4. A dog
5. Round
6. Six
7. Yes
8. Four
9. Toadstools
10. Two

150. Herrerasaurus was Triassic and 2.1m.
Deinonychus was Cretaceous and 1.5m.
Allosaurus was Jurassic and 5m.

152. B and D

153. KENTROSAURUS

154. C

156. SHANBEA

157.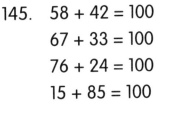

158. 31 + 67 + 20 = 118
18 + 6 + 49 = 73
53 + 12 + 25 = 90
76 + 4 + 100 = 180
48 + 40 + 50 = 138
27 + 27 + 54 = 108

160. Here are some you might have thought of: toe, one, net, tan, use, hens, tune, south, snout, those.

161. 320
16 20
8 2 10
4 2 1 10

162. Seismosaurus was ENORMOUS!

164. C

166.

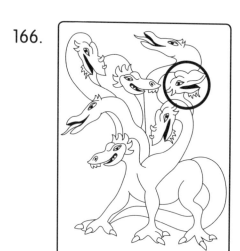

168.

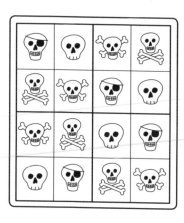

169.

170. 8

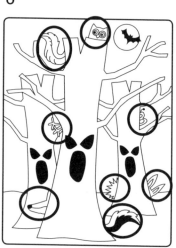

172. MAIASAURA

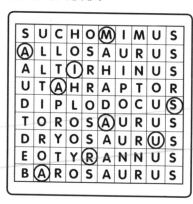

173. STEGO-SNORUS!

174.

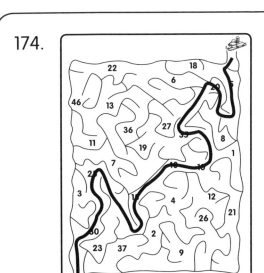

176.

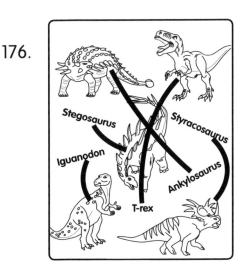

177.
25 X 3 = 75
19 + 26 + 33 = 78
246 ÷ 3 = 82
220 – 89 – 46 = 85
19 x 4 = 76

178. DRACULA, WOLFMAN,
THE BLOB, GREMLINS,
GHOULIES, CRITTERS
The new letters spell the
word HALLOWEEN.

180.

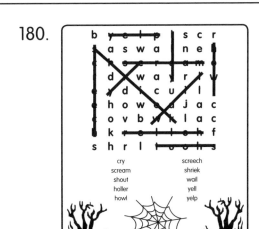

cry   screech
scream   shriek
shout   wail
holler   yell
howl   yelp

181. No
5
10
4 hours
2½ hours

182. C

183. BRICKS

184. B

186. Here are some you might
have thought of: poser, true,
soup, root, sour, pore, route,
tour, tired, ripe.

187.

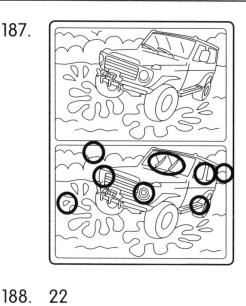

188. 22

190. Don't look, I'm changing!

191. TRICERATOPS, HADROSAUR, MEGALOSAURUS, VELOCIRAPTOR

192.

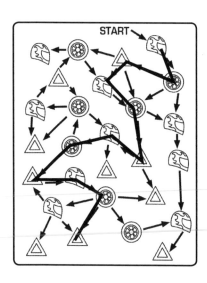

193. 3 and 6

196. They are all hadrosaurs.

198. BULLDOZER

200. DRAGON LIVER
BAT BLOOD
TOAD WARTS
SLUG SLIME

201. PALEONTOLOGIST

202. D

203. ALLOSAURUS,
DEINONYCHUS,
SPINOSAURUS,
VELOCIRAPTOR

204. B

206. C

207.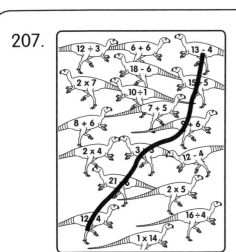

208. 3

210. E

211. A and E

212.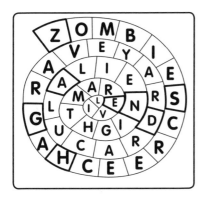

213. 76, 60, 28

214. ROME (Italy), KIEV (Ukraine), OSLO (Norway), BERN (Switzerland), LYON (France)

215.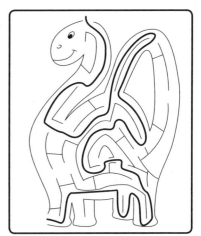

216.

217. B and E

218. THERE IS A NEW FAIR ONE IN THIS LAND. DESTROY HER!

219.

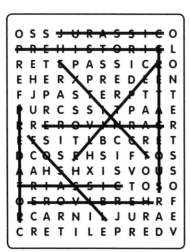

224. BARYONYX

225. 12

220. $100 \div 10 = 10$

$3\frac{1}{2} + 6\frac{1}{2} = 10$

$88 - 78 = 10$

$5 \times 2 = 10$

221. C and F

222. 2 4 8 16 32 64 128 256

3 6 12 24 48 96 192 384

Printed in Malaysia